PEARSON CUSTOM
COMPUTER SCIENCE

DIG 2000 – Introduction to Digital Media
University of Central Florida
Professor Croft

PEARSON

Please visit our website at *www.pearsonlearningsolutions.com.*

Attention Bookstores: For permission to return any unsold stock, contact us at *pe-uscustomreturns@pearson.com.*

Pearson Learning Solutions, 501 Boylston Street, Suite 900, Boston, MA 02116
A Pearson Education Company
www.pearsoned.com

Printed in the United States of America.

ISBN 10: 1-269-66159-0
ISBN 13: 978-1-269-66159-1

Table of Contents

Background

TABLE OF CONTENTS

courtesy of Yue-Ling Wong

Summary   Terms   Learning Aids   Review Questions

KEY CONCEPTS

- Analog information versus digital data
- Converting analog data to digital data: sampling and quantizing
- Bits and bytes
- Base-10 versus base-2
- File size calculation
- File compression

GENERAL LEARNING OBJECTIVES

In this chapter, you will learn

- The computer terms common to digital media fundamentals.
- The difference between analog information and digital data.
- What the binary system means.
- The basic steps of digitization: sampling and quantization.
- The general strategies for reducing digital media file sizes.
- The reasons for file compression and types of file compression.

1 INTRODUCTION

Digital media studies rely on both conceptual and creative knowledge. Although knowing how to use digital media application programs, such as Adobe Photoshop and Corel PaintShop Pro for digital imaging, Adobe Premiere Pro and Apple Final Cut for digital video, and Adobe Audition and Sony Sound Forge for digital audio, is required, understanding the underlying principles and concepts helps to realize a creative idea with predictable results. Simply learning a particular version of a particular program restricts your creativity to what that version of that program can do. If you generalize by associating the task you want to accomplish with the basic concept behind the tool, then when you have to switch to another program or a new version, you can easily look up the information associated with the task in the program's Help menu.

Many application programs provide default settings to create digital media products, allowing you to create a file without any knowledge of digital media fundamentals. For example, it is possible to apply a special effect with a filter without considering how its many settings affect the image. No error message will prevent you from applying the effect and saving the file, but achieving a desired effect often requires some trial-and-error experimenting. Understanding the concepts behind the tools helps you to make rational, educated decisions in using these tools to produce predictable and effective results.

1.1 Relevance of Binary Notation, Bits, and Bytes to Digital Media Studies

This chapter provides the foundational knowledge that is required to understand the more in-depth aspects of digital media. Because computers handle data in the units of bits and bytes, it is inevitable that you will encounter these terms in studying digital media. This chapter will explain the meaning of bits and bytes. It also will explain the conversion between decimal and binary notations. The direct relevance of these concepts to digital media may not be obvious within this chapter alone, but these fundamentals will help you comprehend the terminology you will encounter in studying digital media. For example:

- *File size* and *prefixes*. Digital files—image, sound, and especially video files—can be very large. The file size is often an important consideration that affects your decisions in the creation and export steps. You often will need to monitor your file's size, which is reported in bits and bytes using prefixes (such as kilo, mega, and giga). Bits are then converted to megabytes or gigabytes. Thus, you will need to know how to read a file's size and understand these units.
- *Binary notation*. By learning binary notation and decimal-to-binary conversion, you will see how information actually can be stored and handled on a computer as bits. Understanding the conversion of decimal to binary notations helps you understand why a number, representing a piece of information, requires a certain number of bits to store.
- *Bit depth*. You may have encountered the term *bit depth* or *color depth* if you have worked with digital images. Understanding binary systems helps you comprehend the connection between the bit depth or color depth of an image and the number of colors; for example, 8-bit refers to 256 colors and 24-bit refers to millions of colors.

  With an understanding of bits, you will understand why an image with more colors or higher bit depth has a larger file size.
- *Bit rate*. In working with digital video, you will often encounter the term *bit rate*. The bit rate of a video affects the smoothness of its playback. Understanding bits helps you comprehend what bit rate is, its significance, and how you can calculate your video's average bit rate to predict its playback.
- In Web page creation, you use hexadecimal notation to designate a color for text color and background color. For example, #FF0000 represents red. The conversions from decimal to binary and decimal to hexadecimal notations are similar. What you learn in the conversion of decimal to binary notations also will help you learn how the hexadecimal notation of a color is obtained.

2 ANALOG VERSUS DIGITAL REPRESENTATIONS

It is often said that we live in a digital age. However, the natural world we live in is an analog world. For example, the sounds and music we hear are ***analog*** signals of sound waves. Computers store and transmit information using ***digital*** data. To connect our analog world with computers, analog and digital information must be converted from one form to the other and back again. Unfortunately, the conversion process may sacrifice the exactness of the original information. We will discuss the conversion process—sampling and quantization—in more detail later in this chapter. In order to understand the process, we must first understand the nature of analog and digital representations of information.

2.1 Analog Information

Most information that we perceive in the natural world is in analog form. To illustrate, let's try to measure the length of a pencil (Figure 1). The ruler shows that the pencil is between 7¼ and 7½ inches long, but the point is a little less than halfway between 7¼ and 7½ inches. Would you round it down to 7.25? You cannot reproduce the exact length of this pencil with 7.25 inches. But wait—the pencil tip is about midway between 7¼ and 7½. So should we say it is 7⅜ or 7.375? This measurement is a little closer to the pencil length than 7.25, but the pencil is shorter than 7⅜ inches. So, is it 7.374, 7.373, 7.3735, 7.37355, . . .? An infinite number of divisions exist between two points. How small should the divisions of a ruler be to allow us to make an exact measurement? Infinitely small, because there is always another value between two values!

Figure 1 (a) Measuring the length of a pencil with a ruler. (b) Close-up view of the pencil tip.

Examples of continuous information are time, weight, temperature, lines, waves (such as sound waves), and planes (such as photographs). Analog clocks, thermometers (Figure 2a), and weighing scales are examples of analog devices.

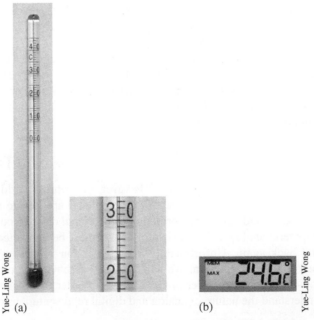

Figure 2 (a) Analog thermometer and its close-up view. (b) Digital thermometer.

2.2 Digital Data

Computers are built from electronic devices that have only two possible states because they are only stable at one of two voltages. Thus, they operate on a binary system, also called base-2. Regardless of the actual voltages of these two states, we might denote them as *off* and *on* or *false* and *true*. In computer science, we denote this pair of states numerically as 0 and 1, respectively.

Most people associate the binary system exclusively with computers. It is true that computers use it, whereas in our daily lives, we use many other numbers. For this reason, many people think it's difficult to understand the binary concept.

However, the binary system is not that difficult. For example, imagine using eye signals to communicate with your friends. Each eye has closed and open positions (Figure 3). When you want to signal your friend, you first will have to assign meaning to the various combinations of open and closed eyes—*encode* the message. Of course, your friend would have to know how to *decode* your signal—that is, interpret the meaning associated with each signal. For example, you may assign "yes" to "closed left eye, open right eye" and "no" to "both eyes closed." There are four open and closed combinations for two eyes. Therefore, you can send four different messages using eye signals. If we assign a numeric value to each of the open and closed eyes—say, open eye as 1 and closed eye as 0—then the four combinations can be represented as 00, 01, 10, and 11.

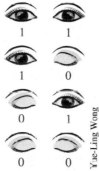

Figure 3 The four combinations of open and closed eyes.

Suppose you want to use eye signals to send your friend a message about a color—one out of 16 different choices. You would need another friend to help because you would need four eyes—a 4-bit system, as in Figure 4. Using two eyes lets you signal your friend a color out of only four different choices.

Let's look at another example using hand signals. Suppose we consider only two possible positions for each finger: raised up or bent down. The number of different combinations with five fingers is $2^5 = 32$. How about with both hands using 10 fingers? $2^{10} = 1024$. Wow! This means that you can send your friend 1024 different messages using the hand signals with each finger either up or down. Of course, some combinations of the raised and bent fingers are quite challenging to make, if not impossible.

Background

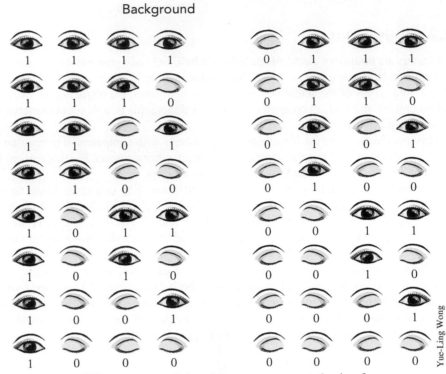

Figure 4 Sixteen different open and closed eye patterns created using four eyes.

3 BITS

In computer systems, data is stored and represented in *b*inary dig*it*s, called **bits**. A bit has two possible values, 0 or 1. In the eye signal example, each eye can be considered a bit, as it can denote two possible states: open or closed. Although the two possible values of a bit are denoted numerically as 0 and 1, they can be used for much more than arithmetic.

One bit is not very useful in representing information, but a combination of bits forming larger sequences can represent content information, such as text characters, color information for digital images, and audio amplitudes.

In the eye signal analogy, each eye is like a bit—it has two states: closed and open, or 0 and 1. Using two eyes, we would call your system a 2-bit system. In the hand signal analogy, if you are using one hand, your system is 5-bit. As you see, the number of possible values corresponds to 2^{bit}.

3.1 Prefixes

Computer file sizes are reported in bits and bytes. Eight bits make a **byte**. Digital files—image, sound, and especially video files—can be very large, and the file size is often an important consideration that affects your decisions in the file creation and export steps. You often will need to look up your files' sizes and monitor the available disk space on your computer's hard drive to make sure you have enough space for new files during the production process.

TABLE I	The Relationship between Sizes and Prefixes under the Base-2 Definition	
Prefix Name	**Abbreviation**	**Size**
Kilo	K	$2^{10} = 1{,}024$
Mega	M	$2^{20} = 1{,}048{,}576$
Giga	G	$2^{30} = 1{,}073{,}741{,}824$
Tera	T	$2^{40} = 1{,}099{,}511{,}627{,}776$
Peta	P	$2^{50} = 1{,}125{,}899{,}906{,}842{,}624$
Exa	E	$2^{60} = 1{,}152{,}921{,}504{,}606{,}846{,}976$
Zetta	Z	$2^{70} = 1{,}180{,}591{,}620{,}717{,}411{,}303{,}424$
Yotta	Y	$2^{80} = 1{,}208{,}925{,}819{,}614{,}629{,}174{,}706{,}176$

Because a file contains lots of bits and bytes, we use prefixes, such as *kilo (K)*, *mega (M)*, *giga (G)*, and *tera (T)*, to better conceive the size. In order for you to correctly interpret the size of your digital media file, you will need to have a clear idea of what these prefixes mean. Table 1 lists the prefixes, abbreviations, and sizes.

DOES A KILO EQUAL 1,000 OR 1,024?

Most people know that 1 kilo equals exactly 1,000 (e.g., 1 kilogram equals 1,000 grams), and the other prefixes imply a number based on 10 to the power of an integer. Notice that under the base-2 definition, a kilobyte (KB) is 1,024 bytes, a megabyte (MB) is 1,048,576 bytes, and so forth (Table 1). This discrepancy has caused confusion among manufacturers of computer storage devices, telecommunication engineers, and the general public.

To avoid such confusion, in December 1998, the International Electrotechnical Commission (IEC) approved the prefixes for binary multiples for use in the fields of data processing and data transmission (Table 2).[*] However, at the time of this writing, these new standard names are not widely used by or known to the public.

TABLE 2	IEC Prefixes for Binary Multiples		
Original	**Prefix Name**	**Symbol**	**Size**
Kilo	Kibi	Ki	$2^{10} = 1{,}024$
Mega	Mebi	Mi	$2^{20} = 1{,}048{,}576$
Giga	Gibi	Gi	$2^{30} = 1{,}073{,}741{,}824$
Tera	Tebi	Ti	$2^{40} = 1{,}099{,}511{,}627{,}776$
Peta	Pebi	Pi	$2^{50} = 1{,}125{,}899{,}906{,}842{,}624$
Exa	Exbi	Ei	$2^{60} = 1{,}152{,}921{,}504{,}606{,}846{,}976$

---

[*] http://physics.nist.gov/cuu/Units/binary.html

With these new standard names and symbols, we have the following:

1 kilobyte = 1,000 bytes
1 kibibyte = 2^{10} bytes = 1,024 bytes
1 megabit = 1,000,000 bits
1 mebibit = 2^{20} bits = 1,048,576 bits

YOUR COMPUTER HARD-DRIVE SPACE

The following exercise shows you how to look up your hard-drive space, both in bytes and gigabytes (GB).

* If you are using Windows, you can right-click on the C: drive in Computer and select Properties. Under the General tab, look up the Used Space and Free Space in bytes and GB. Verify that the numbers match the conversion, according to Tables 1 and 2.
* If you are using Mac OS, select the hard drive, and press Command-I.

For example, say that your computer lists 120,031,539,200 bytes for 111 GB. To convert 120,031,539,200 bytes into GB, you divide 120,031,539,200 by 2^{30} or 1,073,741,824:

$$\frac{120{,}031{,}539{,}200 \text{ bytes}}{1{,}073{,}741{,}824 \text{ bytes/GB}} = 111.8 \text{ GB}$$

The calculation shows you how the number of GB reported is obtained.

4 USING BITS TO REPRESENT NUMERIC VALUES

The mathematics we commonly use is based on the *decimal system*, a *base-10* notation. However, computer systems use *base-2* (the *binary system*), which relates to their basic storage units (bits and bytes) and measures file sizes. By learning what base-2 is and how it works, you will understand how binary notation is used to represent decimal numbers.

4.1 Base-10

The base-10 system uses 10 numerals: 0, 1, 2, 3, 4, 5, 6, 7, 8, and 9. The position of the digits in a number has significance. See the following interpretation of the decimal number 3,872.

$$3872$$
$$3 \times 10^3 + 8 \times 10^2 + 7 \times 10^1 + 2 \times 10^0$$
$$= 3 \times 1000 + 8 \times 100 + 7 \times 10 + 2 \times 1$$
$$= 3000 + 800 + 70 + 2$$
$$= 3872$$

The position of each digit represents a power of 10.

4.2 Base-2

In the binary system, there are only two possible numerals: 0 and 1. In binary notation, the position of each digit represents a power of 2. For example, the binary notation of 1011 can be interpreted as shown here.

$$1011$$
$$1 \times 2^3 + 0 \times 2^2 + 1 \times 2^1 + 1 \times 2^0$$
$$= 1 \times 8 + 0 \times 4 + 1 \times 2 + 1 \times 1$$
$$= 11 \text{ (in decimal notation)}$$

This example shows you how to convert binary notation to decimal notation by breaking it down into products of the power of 2.

Decimal Notation to Binary Notation

Decimal notation can be converted to binary notation through two methods. Either one will give you the same binary representation. We will introduce one method here.

In this method, you repeatedly divide the decimal number by 2 until it becomes 0, noting the remainder of each division. The reverse order of the sequence of the remainders is the binary representation of the decimal number. For example, to convert 19 to binary notation:

> **Base-10 and Base-2** An interactive tutorial explaining base-10 and base-2.

> **Decimal to Binary Guided Practice** An interactive exercise guides you step by step to convert decimal to binary notation. You can practice with a decimal number of your choice or let the program randomly generate one for you.

Division of Number	Remainder
19/2 = 9	1
9/2 = 4	1
4/2 = 2	0
2/2 = 1	0
1/2 = 0	1

The sequence of the remainders you get in the repeated divisions is **11001.** The *reverse* order of this sequence, **10011,** is the binary notation of the decimal number 19.

A "DIGITAL" CLOCK GADGET

A binary coded decimal (BCD) clock (Figure 5) is built with six columns of light-emitting diodes (LEDs). The first two read the hours, the middle two the minutes, and the last two the seconds. An off LED represents 0, and on represents 1.

Background

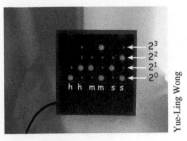

Figure 5 A binary coded decimal (BCD) clock.

The binary notation for the LED pattern shown in Figure 5 is

	0		1		0
	0	0	0	0	1
0	1	1	0	1	0
1	0	0	1	0	1
h	h	m	m	s	s

The bottom row represents 2^0 ($= 1$), the next row up 2^1 ($= 2$) then 2^2 ($= 4$), and then 2^3 ($= 8$).

Each decimal notation for the hour, minute, and second uses two digits. Let's see how the LED pattern representing the hour shown in Figure 5 represents 12.

- The leftmost digit of the hour: The bit pattern for the leftmost digit of the hour is 01. It is converted to 1 in the decimal system because

$$0 \times 2^1 + 1 \times 2^0 = 1$$

- The rightmost digit of the hour: The bit pattern for the rightmost digit of the hour is 0010. It is converted to 2 in the decimal system because

$$0 \times 2^3 + 0 \times 2^2 + 1 \times 2^1 + 0 \times 2^0 = 2$$

Questions

1. Verify that the time shown in Figure 5 is 12:29:25.
2. Explain the number of LEDs available in each column. That is, why are two LEDs sufficient for the first, four needed for the second, and so forth?

5 USING BITS TO REPRESENT NON-NUMERIC VALUES

Although computers use bits to deal with numbers, a sequence of bits can be used to represent almost anything. Recall that you can associate eye signals with "yes" and "no," colors, or even more complicated messages.

TABLE 3		The Lower 128 ASCII Codes													
0	NUL	16	DLE	32		48	0	64	@	80	P	96	`	112	p
1	SOH	17	DC1	33	!	49	1	65	A	81	Q	97	a	113	q
2	STX	18	DC2	34	"	50	2	66	B	82	R	98	b	114	r
3	ETX	19	DC3	35	#	51	3	67	C	83	S	99	c	115	s
4	EOT	20	DC4	36	$	52	4	68	D	84	T	100	d	116	t
5	ENQ	21	NAK	37	%	53	5	69	E	85	U	101	e	117	u
6	ACK	22	SYN	38	&	54	6	70	F	86	V	102	f	118	v
7	REL	23	ETD	39	'	55	7	71	G	87	W	103	g	119	w
8	BS	24	CAN	40	(	56	8	72	H	88	X	104	h	120	x
9	TAB	25	EM	41	)	57	9	73	I	89	Y	105	i	121	y
10	LF	26	SUB	42	*	58	:	74	J	90	Z	106	j	122	z
11	VT	27	ESC	43	+	59	;	75	K	91	[	107	k	123	{
12	FF	28	FS	44	,	60	<	76	L	92	\	108	l	124	|
13	CR	29	GS	45	-	61	=	77	M	93	]	109	m	125	}
14	SO	30	RS	46	.	62	>	78	N	94	^	110	n	126	~
15	SI	31	US	47	/	63	?	79	O	95	_	111	o	127	DEL

The binary system can be used to represent non-numeric information. For example, each letter of the alphabet or other text characters can be represented by a different combination of bits. In the ASCII character set, each character is represented using 8 bits, which permits $2^8 = 256$ different characters. Table 3 shows the lower 128 ASCII codes. The upper 128 values can be used to handle special characters, such as accented characters in foreign languages.

6 THE FINITE AND DISCRETE NATURE OF COMPUTERS

Information in analog media is **continuous** and made up of an *infinite* number of data points. Computers can only handle data that are **discrete** and *finite*. This section will discuss the limitations and advantages of these two properties.

6.1 Limitations

1. As you can see from the eye-signal analogy, the more eyes you use, the more information the signal can represent. With a 2-bit system, we can represent four possible values. If we are representing shades of gray using a 2-bit system, we can only represent four different shades. We can represent 16 different shades with a 4-bit system. The more shades of gray we want to represent, the more bits we need.

To represent colors that change from one point to the next in a natural image would require an infinite number of points, because there are always more points between any two points in the analog world. However, computers have a limit on the number of bits that are

ASCII stands for American Standard Code for Information Interchange. It is an encoding standard for text characters, including the 26-letter English alphabet, and symbols in computer programs.

Another standard is called Unicode, which is not introduced in this chapter. It can represent a large repertoire of multilingual characters.

allowed for each piece of data. A sequence of bits in a computer cannot be infinite. Only a finite set of data can be represented digitally.

2. No matter what the bit limit, each value can only represent one discrete shade of gray. There are always shades of gray in between two consecutive gray values that cannot be captured in digital form.

Thus, the discrete and finite nature of computers restricts the exactness with which analog media—natural sights and sounds—can be captured and reproduced in digital form.

6.2 Advantages

Although digital representation sacrifices exactness in reproducing analog information, its discrete nature offers an advantage in precision, and its finite nature offers an advantage in compactness for media.

INTEGERS AND DECIMAL NUMBERS

Integers are an example of a discrete number system. There is no other integer between any two consecutive integers. Computers can represent integers exactly, because they encode them in the discrete values of 0 and 1. Integers are inherently discrete but they are not inherently finite. A list of integers goes on forever. Although computers can only deal with a finite number of things, handling integers is not a problem, because they set a limit on the number of bits used to represent them.

Numbers with decimal points, such as 0.123, 1.30, and 1.7608, are an example of a continuous number system. Between any two numbers are other numbers. Although these numbers are inherently continuous, computers can handle them by limiting their precision by setting a limit on the number of bits used to represent them. Some such numbers cannot be represented exactly, but only approximately, on computers.

7 CONVERTING ANALOG TO DIGITAL

The conversion of analog information to digital is a two-step process: *sampling* and *quantizing*. Measuring the length of a pencil (Figure 1) illustrates a sampling and quantizing process. For this example, we only sample once; that is, we measure the length of the pencil once. In digital media, you often have to sample more than once, because color value changes over an image's 2-D plane and the amplitude of a sound wave changes over time, for example. In these cases, you must sample multiple times to collect enough information to represent the whole piece. The *sampling rate*—how frequently you take measurements—determines the level of detail at which the collected data can represent the original analog media.

To illustrate the sampling and quantizing steps, let's monitor a puppy's first year of growth by measuring its weight with an analog scale that uses a spring-loaded mechanism to sample the puppy's weight. The more the puppy weighs, the more compressed the spring will be. The spring responds to the extent of compression and rotates the pointer on the scale. This scale is an analog scale, because the spring can be compressed continuously. The reported weight, correspondingly, is analog information.

Background

When you record the weight, you note a discrete number. You have to decide how to round the data, for example, to 0.1, 0.2, or 0.5. The process of rounding a value to one of the discrete values within a set of discrete values is called *quantizing*.

What number would you record for the puppy's weight (Figure 6)? You may choose to round off the reading to the nearest hash mark or estimate the reading between the hash marks. Either way, you may not be recording an exact weight. You sacrifice the accuracy of the measurement when you convert analog information into a discrete number but gain the advantage of reporting the puppy's weight as a precise value—although not necessarily an accurate one. Being distinct and unambiguous, discrete values easily can be processed mathematically, compared, or plotted on a chart. On the other hand, if you record the weight as "somewhere between 5 and 10 pounds," it is not distinct and precise, and you probably will be asked to round it off to a discrete number.

> ⚘ **Converting Analog to Digital—Sampling and Quantizing** An interactive tutorial illustrating the process of sampling and quantizing using a task to monitor a puppy's first year of growth in weight.

Yue-Ling Wong

Figure 6 Sampling a puppy's weight on an analog scale.

In recording a number, you must decide the number of decimal places to use. This will determine the precision of the measurement. Generally, increasing the number of decimal places increases the precision. However, recording the puppy's weight using more decimal places will require more paper and paperwork.

In digitizing analog media, the precision of the data is determined by the number of discrete values, or levels, to which the data can be assigned. Increasing the decimal places is one way to increase the number of levels. For example, allowing one decimal place gives you 10 discrete levels of precision between two consecutive integers; between 2 and 3, there are 2.0, 2.1, 2.2, 2.3, 2.4, 2.5, 2.6, 2.7, 2.8, and 2.9. In digital media, the number of possible levels is called ***bit depth***.

BIT DEPTH DOES NOT MEAN NUMBER OF DECIMAL PLACES

The number of decimal places is used in the simple example of weighing the puppy to illustrate the concept of bit depth. However, increasing the bit depth does not necessarily mean increasing the number of decimal places.

Increasing bit depth means having more discrete levels to which the captured data can be assigned. For 10 discrete levels, you can have the 10 allowable values, as follows:

1. 2.0, 2.1, 2.2, 2.3, 2.4, 2.5, 2.6, 2.7, 2.8, 2.9
2. 0, 5, 10, 15, 20, 25, 30, 35, 40, 45

Using the first 10-level scale for recording the puppy's weight, you get a precision of one decimal place within 2 to 3 pounds. That means that if the puppy's weight is between 2 and 3 pounds, you can distinguish the difference to one decimal place. However, any weight lower than 2.0 will be recorded as 2.0, and any weight higher than 2.9 will be capped at 2.9. The weight obtained from Figure 6 would be recorded as 2.9. If this scale is used, it certainly would not be very useful for tracking the puppy's progress.

Using the second 10-level scale, a weight of 2 pounds would be rounded to 0 and a weight of 3 pounds to 5. The difference between 2 and 3 pounds is altered after they are mapped to the allowable value on this 10-level scale. The difference becomes 5 pounds, not 1 pound. However, because this scale has a wider range, a weight of, say, 45 pounds can be distinguished from 5 pounds. The weight obtained from Figure 6 would have been recorded as 10 pounds if this scale were used. This scale is a better choice than the first for weighing the puppy because a puppy's range of weight falls within the range of scale.

In summary, increasing the number of allowable levels—increasing the bit depth—in digital media can

- Increase the precision of the captured data
- Increase the overall range of the scale
- Increase the file size

Recall that in the eye signal analogy, you need more eyes to encode more choices. Similarly, increasing the number of allowable levels requires more bits to encode a level. Thus, increasing the number of allowable levels increases the file size.

To monitor the puppy's first-year growth by weight, you will have to decide how frequently you want to weigh it. This is the sampling rate. Do you want to weigh it annually, monthly, weekly, daily, or hourly? What factors do you take into consideration when you make this decision?

Based on how fast a puppy normally grows in the first year, weighing it monthly or weekly is reasonable. However, if you do not know how fast a puppy should normally grow, you probably feel a little lost when you are asked to choose how frequently to weigh it. If you sample too infrequently, you will miss critical details that show how the weight changes over time. In that case, how frequently do you sample so that you do not miss any information at all?

As mentioned earlier, when converting analog to digital data, no matter how high the sampling rate is, some analog information will be missed. If you sample too frequently, you will be busy weighing the puppy, and will need more paper to keep the records, more shelf space to store the records, and more time to read through the records later (besides annoying the puppy).

By analogy, if you increase the sampling rate, you increase the accuracy in digitally representing the original analog media. The computer has to sample faster, and the resulting file will have more samples or data. Files will be larger and require more time to process, which may cause noticeable delay in opening or editing the file.

What sampling rate should we use, then? There is no one strictly right or wrong sampling rate. The optimal sampling rate for your purpose will depend on the source content (for example, the rate of change of the original analog source), its intended use, and technical limitations (for example, limitations on the file size and your computer speed). In weighing the puppy, either monthly or weekly seems a reasonable sampling rate. Weekly data may represent the first few months' rapid growth rate more accurately but may yield redundant information in later months. In real life, you can choose to sample the first month's weight more frequently than that of the other months if you anticipate more dramatic changes. You can change the sampling rate in a task. However, in digital media, one sampling rate is normally set for a session.

How is this analogy related to digital media, such as images and sound? In general, the sampling rate for digital images is related to the image resolution (or amount of detail). Quantization is related to the image's bit depth or color depth, which affects the number of colors allowed in the image. For digital audio, quantization also is related to the bit depth, which determines how well the differences in sound amplitude can be represented, and the sampling rate relates to how frequently the amplitude is sampled.

7.1 Problems in Representing Analog Media on Computers

Sound and pictures are by nature continuous phenomena. Each piece of sound or picture is made up of an infinite amount of information. Due to the finite and discrete way that computers handle data, two inevitable problems arise when we want to represent sound and pictures on a computer:

1. Because computers operate on discrete values, the sampling step is required to choose some discrete samples of the information. In addition, computers have only finite capacity, so the sampling rate has to be finite.
2. A computer cannot represent numbers with infinite precision. Thus, the precision with which we represent colors or sounds is limited. Quantization maps the values of the samples to a discrete scale, that is, rounded to an allowable discrete value in the scale.

8 FILE SIZES

In a text document that uses ASCII code to represent text characters, each byte stores an ASCII code that corresponds to a character. The more characters in a text document, the more bytes are required to store the file.

ACTIVITY/EXERCISE

Using Windows 95, 98, 2000, XP, or 7: Open a new text file in Notepad and type the sentence, "Eight bits make a byte." Save the file as file-size-exercise.txt. Then to look at its file size, right-click on the file-size-exercise.txt file and select Properties. You should find that the file size is 23 bytes because there are 23 characters in this sentence—1 byte for each character (including spaces, which are characters, too). What is the ASCII code for a space? Look it up in Table 3.

Using Mac OS X: Open a new text file in TextEdit and type the sentence, "Eight bits make a byte." Select Format > Make Plain Text. Then save the file as file-size-exercise.txt. In the Save dialog box, choose Western for the Plain Text Encoding. Verify that the file size is 23 bytes.

Questions

In the file-size-exercise.txt file you created, add a blank line at the end of the sentence by hitting the Enter (Windows) or Return (Mac) key on your keyboard. Save the file. Then look at its file size again. What is the file size now? By how many byte(s) has it increased?

Creating a blank line in Notepad actually involves both a carriage return (CR) and a line feed (LF). Are they characters? Look them up in Table 3.

If you create a Microsoft Word document with the same sentence ("Eight bits make a byte."), will the file size also be 23 bytes? No. It is larger because other information (such as text formatting) is saved with the file.

A byte is not just for storing a character in a text document. A byte is 8 bits, with 256 possible values. It can be used for many purposes. If you use a byte to store the color information of each pixel in an image, then each pixel can be assigned with one of 256 colors that the image allows. Color images use more than one byte per pixel to represent color information if each pixel has more than 256 choices of color. The more bytes per pixel, the more bytes are needed to store the image, and the larger the file size. Thus, an image with more allowable colors has a larger file size. Whether one or more bytes are used for each pixel, the file size also increases with the number of pixels in an image. The more pixels an image has, the more bytes are needed to store the image, and the larger the file size.

Multimedia files—image, sound, and especially video files—can be very large and require tremendous amounts of storage space. In addition, the larger the file, the longer the transmission time to send it over the Internet and the longer the processing time. Longer processing time means that it may take longer for your audience to open your files and slow down your productivity when you are editing the file.

Generally, there are three strategies to reduce the size of a digital media file:

- Reduce the sampling rate
- Reduce the bit depth
- Apply file compression

When you reduce the sampling rate and bit depth, the resemblance between the resulting digital image and the original subject will be reduced, and digital audio quality may be noticeably degraded. In working with digital media files, you often have to weigh quality against file size.

9 COMPRESSION

File compression lets you reduce the total number of bits and bytes in a file. Reducing the file size allows a file to be transmitted faster over a network and take up less storage space. Nowadays, storage space is inexpensive, and many people have access to a high-speed network, but you still have to consider the playback performance of video files. Uncompressed videos require a very high data rate. Video playback will become jerky and skip frames if the computer cannot process the video data fast enough. If the data rate of a video on the Internet is too high for the network speed, video playback will also become choppy because it has to pause frequently to wait for enough data to be transmitted over the Internet. In addition to the waiting time for the Internet transfer, another factor you may want to consider is the cost of the data access. Many wireless carriers implement a limit on their data access plans. It costs the subscribers extra when they go beyond the data limit of their subscription plan.

There are some common data compression methods applied to multimedia files. Some are not specific to multimedia files. Others are available only for a certain category of media files. For example, Sorenson is available for creating QuickTime movies but not for sound compression.

By learning the concepts behind these compression methods, you will understand the strengths and weaknesses of each. Some allow you to control certain parameters when saving a file in a multimedia application. Understanding what these parameters mean and how they affect the quality of your files will help you make decisions that are best for your multimedia work.

✏ **Video Examples of Different Levels of Compression: Uncompressed, Low Compression, and High Compression** These sample videos are 60-frame computer animations, rendered frame by frame (720 × 480 pixels) as an image sequence, imported in Adobe Premiere Pro, and exported as QuickTime and MPEG-2 movies. Each exported movie uses a different compressor.

- QuickTime, uncompressed (Note: This file takes longest to download and has the least smooth playback.)
- QuickTime, using Animation Codec
- QuickTime, using H.264 Codec
- QuickTime, using Sorenson Video 3 Codec
- MPEG-2
- MPEG-4

Note the following properties of each movie:

1. Image quality for different codecs
2. File sizes
3. Smoothness of playback

Why are the image quality, file size, and playback different with different compressors?

9.1 Lossy and Lossless Compression

Compression methods can be categorized as either lossy or lossless. With *lossy compression*, some information in the original file will be lost and cannot be recovered. JPEG, a popular image file format for Web images, is an example of lossy compression. MP3, a popular file format for digital audio, is another example of lossy compression. Many video codecs are also lossy, although a few use lossless algorithms. For files that you want to keep as the start file for further editing, you should avoid applying lossy compression. The exception is video files, which are normally applied with lossy compression.

For details on the compression algorithms, see the CS Module.

10 SUMMARY

The analog information we perceive through our senses is continuous and infinite. However, computers store and transmit information using discrete, finite data, which presents some limitations but also advantages in capturing and reproducing analog media.

Converting from analog to digital data involves a two-step process—sampling and quantizing. How frequently an analog medium is sampled during the sampling step is called the sample rate. For example, the sample rate in digital imaging determines the resolution of a digital image. In the quantization step, the number of discrete levels used to map the samples' values is called the bit depth. For example, the bit depth of a digital image specifies the number of colors available in the image. The discrete and finite nature of computers restricts the precision with which analog media—natural sights and sounds—can be reproduced in digital form. In converting from analog to digital, we sacrifice exactness.

Because of the current electronic technology that computer systems are built on, they operate on the binary system, which uses base-2 notation. Only two numerals are available in base-2, denoted as 0 and 1 in the language of computers. Base-10 can be converted to base-2 notation and vice versa. For example, the binary notation for the decimal number 19 is 10011.

Multimedia files—image, sound, and especially video files—can be very large. Such large file sizes can require tremendous amounts of storage space. In addition, the larger the file, the longer it takes to send the file over the Internet.

Generally, there are three strategies to reduce the size of a digital media file:

- Reduce the sampling rate
- Reduce the bit depth
- Apply file compression

Reducing the sampling rate or bit depth reduces the resemblance between your resulting digital media and the original analog media. When working with digital media files, you often have to weigh the quality against the file size. Compression methods can be categorized as either lossy or lossless. With lossy compressions, such as JPEG and MP3, some information in the original file will be lost and cannot be recovered. Whenever possible, you should avoid using this type of compression for any file that you want to keep as the start file for further editing.

TERMS

analog	decimal system	kilo (K)
base-10	decode	lossy compression
base-2	digital	mega (M)
binary system	discrete	quantizing
bit depth	encode	sampling
bits	file compression	sampling rate
byte	finite	tera (T)
continuous	giga (G)	

LEARNING AIDS

The following learning aids can be found at the text's companion Web site.

🖰 **Base-10 and Base-2**

An interactive tutorial explaining base-10 and base-2.

🖰 **Decimal to Binary Guided Practice**

An interactive exercise guides you step by step to convert decimal to binary notation. You can practice with a decimal number of your choice or let the program randomly generate one for you.

🖰 **Binary Coded Decimal (BCD) Clock**

This shows a BCD clock in action. It could be fun to race to decode the time, as the LED patterns change by the second.

🖰 **Converting Analog to Digital—Sampling and Quantizing**

An interactive tutorial illustrating the process of sampling and quantizing using a task to monitor a puppy's first year of growth in weight.

✏️ **Video Examples of Different Levels of Compression: Uncompressed, Low Compression, and High Compression**

These sample videos are 60-frame computer animations, rendered frame by frame (720 × 480 pixels) as an image sequence, imported in Adobe Premiere Pro, and exported as QuickTime and MPEG-2 movies. Each exported movie uses a different compressor.

- QuickTime, uncompressed (*Note:* This file takes longest to download and has the least smooth playback.)
- QuickTime, using Animation Codec
- QuickTime, using H.264 Codec
- QuickTime, using Sorenson Video 3 Codec
- MPEG-2
- MPEG-4

Note the following properties of each movie:

1. Image quality for different codecs
2. File sizes
3. Smoothness of playback

Why are the image quality, file size, and playback different with different compressors?

REVIEW QUESTIONS

When applicable, please select all correct answers.

1. Digital data is _____ and analog information is _____.
   A. continuous; discrete
   B. discrete; continuous

2. Digitization means converting _____ into _____.

3. Converting from analog to digital involves a two-step process: _____ and _____.

4. When analog information is converted to digital data, we must consider two properties that affect the exactness of the digital representation, one from sampling and one from quantizing. Which of the following is from sampling?

A. Sampling rate
B. Bit depth

5. Which of the following refers to the number of allowable levels of digitized data?

A. Sampling rate
B. Bit depth

6. Which of the following can reduce the file size of digital media?

A. Decrease sampling rate
B. Increase sampling rate
C. Decrease bit depth
D. Increase bit depth

7. Our everyday decimal numbering system is base-_____. Computers use base-_____, which is also known as the _____ numbering system.

8. The smallest unit in a binary system is a _____,

A. bit
B. byte

which refers to a binary digit (i.e., a _____ or a _____). (Enter a digit or number.)

9. Fill in the blanks with "bit(s)" or "byte(s)": Eight _____ equals one _____.

10. The word *bit* comes from the shortening of the words _____ and _____.

11. If you want to use hand signals to communicate only two possibilities—yes or no— to your friend, what is the minimum number of fingers you need? _____ We may call this hand-signal system _____-bit.

12. A pixel that can have only one of two possible color values requires _____ bit(s) to store the color information.

13. If you use a byte to store the grayscale information of each pixel in a grayscale image, how many gray levels are possible for each pixel?

14. How many bits are in the binary notation 0011010? How many possible values can this many bits represent?

15. Which of the following sizes is the largest?

A. 24 GB
B. 24 MB
C. 240 MB
D. 2,400 KB

16. Fill in the names and abbreviations for the following:

Name	Abbr.	Size in bytes
Kilobytes	KB	$2^{10} = 1{,}024$
		$2^{20} = 1{,}048{,}576$
		$2^{30} = 1{,}073{,}741{,}824$
		$2^{40} = 1{,}099{,}511{,}627{,}776$

17. How many bits is each of the following binary numbers? Also, convert each to a decimal number.

   i. 00000000
   ii. 0000
  iii. 01101000
  iv. 0110100
   v. 11
  vi. 111
 vii. 0000000000000010

18. Convert the following decimal numbers into binary.

   i. 0
   ii. 1
  iii. 2
  iv. 3
   v. 12
  vi. 123
 vii. 11
viii. 111
  ix. 128
   x. 255

19. i. Name three general strategies to reduce the size of a digital media file.
   ii. Which of these strategies does not necessarily sacrifice the quality of the media file? Why?

20. You should avoid using lossy compression for any file that you want to keep as the start file for further editing because _____.

Fundamentals of Digital Imaging

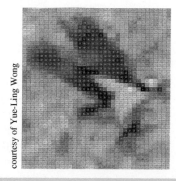

courtesy of Yue-Ling Wong

Summary   Terms   Learning Aids   Review Questions

From Chapter 2 of *Digital Media Primer and Digital Audio, Video, Imaging and Multimedia Programming*, Second Edition.
Yue-Ling Wong. Copyright © 2013 by Pearson Education, Inc. All rights reserved.

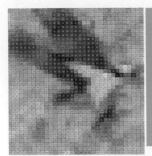
courtesy of Yue-Ling Wong

1 INTRODUCTION

Digitization of analog information involves a two-step process: sampling and quantizing. Digitization of any digital medium—images, sound, or videos—always involves these two steps. However, if you have worked with digital image processing programs, you may have noticed that you never encounter the terms "sampling" and "quantizing" explicitly in the program. On the other hand, you may have already heard about pixels, resolution, and bit depth. So, what do sampling and quantizing have to do with pixels, resolution, and bit depth? In this chapter, we are going to discuss the relationships among these fundamental concepts and their applications in digital imaging.

To understand pixels, resolution, and bit depth, we need to start with the concepts of sampling and quantizing. In fact, it is only by means of the two-step process of digitization that we ever arrive at pixels, resolution, and bit depth in digital imaging. Although you may not encounter the terms when you use digital imaging applications to work with pixels or manipulate the resolution or bit depth of digital images, you are applying the concepts of sampling and quantizing. Understanding these fundamental concepts and how they are applied to digital images will help you take full advantage of digital media tools and produce predictable results effectively in your creative process.

2 DIGITIZING IMAGES

Look up and let your eyes fall on the scene in front of you. Draw an imaginary rectangle around what you see. This is your "viewfinder." Imagine that you are going to capture this view on a pegboard. Why a pegboard, you may ask? A pegboard is a good analogy for a digitized image because each peg hole represents a *discrete sample*. In the following sections we will use the pegboard analogy to discuss sampling and quantization in detail.

> ⏻ Sampling and Quantizing in Digital Images An interactive tutorial, complementary to the materials covered in Sections 2.1 and 2.2, explains sampling and quantizing in digitizing an image.

2.1 Step 1: Sampling

The natural scenes you see in the world around you are colored in continuous tones. There is no sharp division between one point of color and the next. Each point blends continuously into the next. In this respect, color is an analog phenomenon in human perception. In order to put it into a language that computers can understand, color must be digitized.

> ⏻ Pegboard and Resolution An interactive tutorial using the pegboard as an analogy to explain resolution in capturing and displaying digital images.

The first step of the digitization process is **sampling**, a process by which you record or sample the color in a natural image at discrete, evenly spaced points. Let's say that Figure 1a represents the natural image that you want to capture as a digital image with a digital camera.

Say this image is going to be sampled into a grid of 25 × 20 discrete samples (Figure 1b). Using the pegboard analogy, we could say that this image is going to be re-created on a pegboard with 25 × 20 peg holes. The color of each of these discrete samples is averaged to a single uniform value to represent the corresponding area in the image (Figure 1c). This 25 × 20 sampled image looks blocky. Details are lost because the grid is too coarse for this image.

In digital imaging, each of these discrete sample points is called a **picture element**, or **pixel** for short. Each pixel stores the color information of the corresponding position on the image. The position is defined by its horizontal and vertical coordinates. **Pixel dimensions** refer to the image's width and height in pixels. The dimensions of your resulting digitized image in pixels will be 25 pixels × 20 pixels. In the pegboard analogy, the dimensions of your image in pegs would be 25 pegs × 20 pegs. Note that 25 pixels and 20 pixels are by no means realistic pixel dimensions in digital photography; they are only for illustration purposes here. Most digital cameras can capture images of over several thousand pixels in each dimension—for example, 3,000 pixels × 2,000 pixels.

There are two methods of capturing digital images—scanning and digital photography. The concept of sampling and quantizing applies to both methods, not just digital photography.

MEGAPIXEL

Often, the word **megapixel** is associated with the features of a digital camera. One megapixel is equal to 1,000,000 pixels. The total number of pixels in a 3,000 × 2,000-pixel digital image is

$$3,000 \text{ pixels} \times 2,000 \text{ pixels} = 6,000,000 \text{ pixels}$$

This is sometimes referred to as 6 megapixels.

(a)

(b)

(c)

(d)

(e)

Figure 1 (a) A natural image. (b) Imagine a grid of 25 × 20 cells is applied on the image. (c) The color of each of the 25 × 20 grid cells is averaged to a single value. (d) Imagine a grid of 100 × 80 cells is applied on the image. (e) The color of each of the 100 × 80 grid cells is averaged to a single value. This image can be found on the insert.

How frequently you take a sample is defined by the sampling rate. The words "frequency" and "rate" are often associated with time. However, for an image, *frequency* refers to how close neighboring samples are in a 2-D image plane. If you sample the image with a finer grid than in the previous example, say 100×80 (Figures 1d and 1e), you are using a higher sampling rate because you are sampling more frequently within the same spatial distance. In digital imaging, increasing the sampling rate increases the image ***resolution***. With higher resolution, you have more samples (pixels) to represent the same scene and thus you capture more details from the original scene (Figure 2). The pixel dimensions of the captured image are increased, and so is the file size of the digitized image.

(a)   (b)

Figure 2 The relative sizes of an image 25 pixels $\times$ 20 pixels (left) and 100 pixels $\times$ 80 pixels (right) captured from the same scene. ▄ This image can be found on the insert.

A PIXEL IS A PIXEL IS A POINT SAMPLE—NOT A LITTLE SQUARE BLOCK

When you zoom in on a digital image in an image editing program, you often see the pixels represented as little square blocks. However, keep in mind that a pixel is a sample at a single point; it is a point sample that does not really have a *physical* dimension associated with it.

2.2 Step 2: Quantizing

A natural image is colored in continuous tones, and thus it theoretically has an infinite number of colors. The discrete and finite language of the computer restricts the reproduction of an infinite number of colors and shades. The process of mapping an infinite number of possibilities—that is, an infinite number of colors and shades in the case of digital imaging—to a finite list of numbers—that is, a finite number of color codes in the case of digital imaging—is called ***quantization***.

Before mapping the color of each pixel to a discrete and precise value, you need to consider how many possible colors you want to use in the image. To illustrate this process, let's revisit the example of the sampled image in Figure 1 and continue on to the quantization step.

Suppose the color of each sample in the 100-pixels × 80-pixels image (Figure 1e) is quantized into one of four discrete colors (Figure 3a) by mapping it to the closest color. Figure 4a shows the resulting quantized image. This 4-color palette obviously does not provide sufficient color levels for this scene.

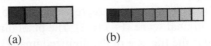

(a)   (b)

Figure 3 (a) A 4-color palette. (b) An 8-color palette. ▨ This image can be found on the insert.

Yue-Ling Wong (a)   (b)   Yue-Ling Wong

Figure 4 The sampled image is quantized into (a) four colors, and (b) eight colors. ▨ This image can be found on the insert.

The image fidelity and details are lost because different colors from the original are now mapped to the same color on the palette. For example, the area in the outlined square in Figure 5b is made up of many different green colors. The same area in the 4-color image (Figure 5a) now has only one color. The details that rely on the subtle color differences are lost during quantization.

YOU MAY ASK: WHY THE CHOICE OF THOSE FOUR OR EIGHT PARTICULAR COLORS?

The palette does not have to be restricted to those exact four or eight colors. The 4-color and 8-color palettes in this example all contain shades of green because the original scene is mainly green. However, you do not have to use only green colors for a scene like this. For any images, no matter what colors you choose, the bit depth for four colors is always 2 bits, and the bit depth for eight colors is always 3 bits. The actual colors included in the palette, however, may vary depending on the user's choice.

(a)

(b)

Yue-Ling Wong

Yue-Ling Wong

Figure 5 (a) The colors in the original image (b) are quantized into four colors using the palette shown in Figure 3a. Some of the similar green colors, such as those in the outlined square box, are now mapped to a single color. ▇▇ This image can be found on the insert.

The number of colors used for quantization is related to the **color depth** or **bit depth** of the digital image. A bit depth of n allows 2^n different colors. Therefore, a 2-bit digital image allows 2^2 (i.e., 4) colors in the image.

USING BINARY BITS TO REPRESENT COLORS ON COMPUTERS

Internally, a computer uses the binary system to represent colors. For example, for 2-bit color, the binary bits for the four colors are 00, 01, 10, and 11.

Bit 2	Bit 1
0	0
0	1
1	0
1	1

Then, will increasing the number of colors in the palette improve the image fidelity? The answer is: it depends, and in most cases, yes. The number of colors or the bit depth is not the only determining factor for image fidelity in quantizing an image; the choice of colors for the quantization also plays an important role in the reproduction of an image.

To illustrate the importance of the choice of colors in the palette, let's increase the bit depth to 3 (2^3 = 8 colors). An 8-color palette (Figure 6a) that is drastically different from the overall colors of the original natural image will be used. The resulting quantized image with this new palette is shown in Figure 6b.

The 8-color image (Figure 6b) that is quantized using a drastic 8-color palette does not look any closer to the original scene than the 4-color one (Figure 4a) that is quantized

Yue-Ling Wong (a)   (b)   Yue-Ling Wong

Figure 6 (a) Using a different 8-color palette, (b) the sampled image is quantized. ▄▄ This image can be found on the insert.

using a 4-color palette made up of green shades. Although the larger palette increases the image detail a little in certain areas—for example, in the sky and the water areas—by allowing more levels of color distinction, the colors are not faithful to the original image.

24-BIT, 32-BIT, AND 48-BIT COLOR DEPTH

A single 8-bit byte can be used to represent one of 256 different possible values. The values range from 0 to 255. An RGB (red, green, blue) color can be represented in three 8-bit bytes, one byte for each component of the R, G, and B. Thus, in this case, the color depth is *24 bits,* which means it allows $2^{24} = 16,777,216$ colors. Each of the R, G, and B components allows 2^8 levels—that is, 256 levels (from 0 to 255).

Although 24-bit color is often sufficient for human vision to represent colors, as computer processors get faster and storage media get cheaper, higher color depth (such as 48-bit color) is increasingly supported by scanners and image editing programs. Forty-eight-bit RGB color is represented using 16 bits per component of R, G, and B.

Questions*

1. How many possible colors can be represented with 48-bit color depth?
2. How many possible levels of red can be represented with 48-bit RGB color?
3. How many times would a file size increase by going from 24-bit to 48-bit color?

A *32-bit* image is basically 24-bit RGB with an additional 8-bit alpha channel. The alpha channel is used to specify the level of transparency. Unlike 24-bit images that are fully opaque, 32-bit images can be smoothly blended with other images.

Question

4. How many levels of transparency does an 8-bit alpha channel allow?

----

* Answers to Questions: (1) 2^{48}; (2) 2^{16}; (3) double; (4) 2^8, i.e., 256.

3 BITMAPPED IMAGES

Each pixel contains the color information using numeric values, which can be represented by a sequence of bits—1s and 0s. A 1-bit image allows two (2^1) colors, which can be represented by 1 and 0. The digit 1 can be used to designate a particular color and 0 another color. For example, a simple single-color diagonal line on a solid-color background can be represented in 1s and 0s, as shown in Figure 7.

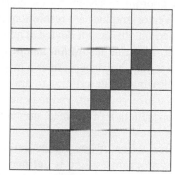

1	1	1	1	1	1	1	1
1	1	1	1	1	1	1	1
1	1	1	1	1	1	0	1
1	1	1	1	1	0	1	1
1	1	1	1	0	1	1	1
1	1	1	0	1	1	1	1
1	1	0	1	1	1	1	1
1	1	1	1	1	1	1	1

Yue-Ling Wong

Figure 7 For each pixel in a 1-bit (i.e., 2-color) bitmap image, its color value can be represented by 0s and 1s. ▪▪ This image can be found on the insert.

Digital images described by pixel values such as the one shown in Figure 7 are called **bitmapped** images. The term *bitmapping* refers to how these bits representing the image are stored in computer memory. Bitmapped images also are called **raster graphics**. The term *rastering* refers to the way most video displays translate the images into a series of horizontal lines on the screen.

Bitmapped images commonly are used in image editing applications. Because they are composed of pixels, the image content can be edited pixel by pixel easily. However, their size and appearance depend on their output resolution to the device, for example, dots per inch for a monitor and pixels per inch for a printer. Bitmapped images can appear jagged when they're scaled up onscreen or printed at a low resolution.

In certain contexts, a bitmap refers to an image with 1 bit per pixel; that is, each pixel has a value of either 0 or 1. The term *pixmap* is used for the image that uses more than 1 bit for each pixel; that is, the image has more than two colors. In this text, the term *bitmap* or *bitmapped images* refers to all pixel-based images.

4 VECTOR GRAPHICS

Besides using pixels to describe digital images, there is another way to create imagery—it is to describe the graphic mathematically. This type of digital image is called a **vector graphic**. For example, to describe a line like the one in Figure 8, you can use a simple equation. Using equations to represent graphics is more concise than bitmapping. Consider this analogy in the context of getting directions for a trip: Bitmapped images are like getting driving directions on a printed Google map. Vector graphics, on the other hand, are analogous to written directions. Instead of tracing out a route on a map, someone could give you written directions that say, for example, "Head southwest on N Main St toward W Dalton Rd. When you come to the stoplight, turn right. Go past the mall and turn at the first entrance to the restaurant." It may take you more time to translate the written directions into a mental image of where you're going, as compared to understanding a map that is already in visual form. An advantage of the written directions, however, is that they might actually be more concise and require less space than a full printed map.

Similarly, vector graphics are generally more concise descriptions of digital images than bitmaps are. But the most distinct advantage of vector graphics is that they are resolution independent. Let's explain what resolution independence means and what characteristic of vector graphics makes them resolution independent.

In contrast to bitmapped images that already have the number of pixels or resolution specified when they are stored, vector graphics do not use pixels but equations. The images of vector graphics are produced for output or display by calculating the points, according to the equations that make up the graphics. The coordinate system for the equations is arbitrary. That is, its scale can be set to any level. Vector graphics are resolution independent because they can be scaled to any size and printed on any output device at any resolution, without losing detail or clarity in the picture. To illustrate resolution independence, let's return to the analogy of driving directions versus a map. You can produce a map from written directions at any size you want simply by following the description to draw on any size of paper. However, to scale a printed map into the size you want, you may need to rescale it on a photocopier. This will produce a fuzzy reproduction of the map, no matter whether you are blowing it up or shrinking it down.

Examples of vector graphic application programs are Adobe Illustrator, Adobe Flash, and CorelDRAW.

Consider a simple example of vector graphics, a line. A line can be described mathematically with an equation. In vector graphic programs, a line is defined by two end points (Figure 8a). A line can be stroked at a certain width, but it is still a vector graphic. When you zoom in on the line on a computer display, the line is still clear (Figure 8b). When the line is rasterized to a bitmapped image at a low resolution, as shown in Figure 8c, zooming in on the line will show that it is jagged. If the same vector graphic line is rasterized to a bitmapped image at a higher resolution setting (Figure 8d), the rasterized line appears smoother than the one from the lower resolution, although it still appears jagged.

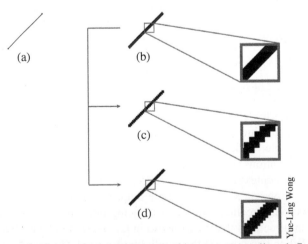

Figure 8 Vector graphics and rasterized bitmapped images: (a) A line defined by two end points. (b) The line stroked at a certain width. (c) The line rasterized at a low resolution. (d) The line rasterized at a higher resolution.

RASTERIZING VECTOR GRAPHICS

Most vector graphics programs let you **rasterize,** or convert, vector graphics into pixel-based bitmapped images. Because you are making a resolution-independent vector graphic into a resolution-dependent image, you need to specify a resolution for rasterizing, that is, how coarse or how fine the sampling.

The rasterized image will appear jagged. This jagged effect is a form of **aliasing** caused by undersampling or insufficient sampling rate. In addition, as you see in Figure 9b, the high contrast between black and white pixels makes the effect very noticeable. To soften the jaggedness, we can color the pixels with intermediary shades in the areas where the sharp color changes occur (Figure 9c). This technique is called **anti-aliasing**. With the same raster resolution setting, you can make the rasterized graphics appear smoother with anti-aliasing than without.

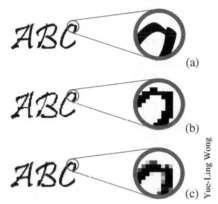

(a)

(b)

(c)

Yue-Ling Wong

Figure 9 Vector graphics versus rasterized graphics: (a) Edges still appear smooth at higher magnification. (b) Rasterized vector graphic without anti-aliasing. (c) Rasterized vector graphic with anti-aliasing.

5 FILE TYPES OF DIGITAL IMAGES

The file types you will most commonly see and use are given in the Tables 1 and 2.

6 DIGITAL IMAGE FILE SIZE AND OPTIMIZATION

An image with a higher resolution or higher bit depth has a larger file size. Thus, to reduce the storage space requirement and allow faster download over the Internet, the file size of an image may be reduced by lowering its resolution or bit depth. However, if the image resolution and bit depth have to be maintained, the file size of an image can be reduced by applying compression.

TABLE I	Common File Types of Bitmapped or Pixel-Based Images			
File Type	**File Suffix**	**Standard Color Modes**	**Use**	**Compression**
JPEG (Joint Photographic Experts Group)	.jpg or .jpeg	RGB, CMYK	• Best for continuous-tone images, such as photographs • Can be used for Web images	Lossy compression method called JPEG compression that works well with photographs
GIF (Graphics Interchange Format)	.gif	Indexed color, grayscale	• Supports up to 8-bit color, best for illustration graphics or cartoon-like pictures with large areas of solid color and clear divisions between color areas • A proprietary format of CompuServe • Can be used for Web images • Allows transparency of one designated color	Lossless compression method called LZW compression
PNG (Portable Network Graphics)	.png	RGB, indexed, grayscale, black and white	• Supports 8-bit and 24-bit color • Can be used for Web images • Allows variable transparency	Lossless compression
PICT (Macintosh Picture Format)	.pict	RGB, indexed, grayscale, black and white	Used on Mac OS	Allows JPEG compression
BMP (Bitmapped Picture)	.bmp	RGB, indexed, grayscale, black and white	Used on Windows	Allows run-length encoding compression (lossless)
TIFF (Tag Image File Format)	.tif or .tiff	RGB, CMYK, CIE-Lab, indexed, grayscale, black and white	• Supported on both Windows and Mac OS • A common file format for digital imaging • Supports alpha channel and layers	Allows uncompressed, LZW compression (lossless), ZIP (lossless), and JPEG (lossy)
PSD (Photoshop Digital Image)	.psd	RGB, CMYK, CIE-Lab, indexed, grayscale, black and white	• Proprietary format of Adobe Photoshop • Good for any types of digital images that Photoshop supports • Stores layers • Supports alpha channel	Lossless compression

TABLE 2	Common File Types of Vector Graphics	
File Type	**File Suffix**	**Information and Use**
Encapsulated PostScript	.eps	Standard file format for storing and exchanging files in professional printing
Adobe Illustrator file	.ai	
Adobe Flash file	.fla, .swf	
Windows Metafile format	.wmf	Many clip arts from Microsoft Office are in this format
Enhanced Metafile format	.emf	Developed by Microsoft as a successor to .wmf

Let's look at the file size of a typical digital photograph without compression. A 6-megapixel digital camera can produce digital images of 3,000 × 2,000 pixels in 24-bit color depth. The uncompressed file size can be computed as follows:

Total pixels: 3,000 × 2,000 pixels = 6,000,000 pixels

File size in bits: 6,000,000 pixels × 24 bits/pixel = 144,000,000 bits

File size in bytes: 144,000,000 bits/(8 bits/byte) = 18,000,000 bytes

An uncompressed 6-megapixel image would require 144,000,000 bits, which is 18,000,000 bytes of disk space. There are three ways to reduce the file size of a digital image—reduce its pixel dimensions, lower its bit depth, and compress the file.

(1) **Reducing the pixel dimensions:**

This can be achieved by either of the following:

(a) Capture the image at a lower resolution in the first place.
- If you are capturing the image by scanning, use a lower scanning dpi. The scanned image will have smaller pixel dimensions.
- If you are capturing the image by digital photography and your camera has an option for the image size, you can set a smaller image size—lowering the pixel dimensions of the digital photo.

(b) Resample, or scale, the existing digital image to lower pixel dimensions.

As you see in the file size calculation, the file size is directly proportional to the number of pixels in an image. This means that reducing the number of pixels in half will lower the file size to half of the original.

Exercise[*]: The pixel dimensions of the image used in this example of file size calculation are 3,000 × 2,000 pixels. If you scale both the width and height of this image to half (i.e., 1,500 × 1,000 pixels), how much will the file size be reduced?

The destined pixel dimension you choose depends on the amount of detail you need in your image and your intended use of the image—that is, whether you intend to print out the picture or display it on a computer. Lowering the pixel dimension sacrifices the image detail, which affects the image quality. Therefore, in reducing the pixel dimension to reduce file size, you need to weigh the image detail against the file size.

---

[*]**Answer:** The number of pixels in the original image = 3,000 × 2,000 = 6,000,000. The number of pixels in the resized image = 1,500 × 1,000 = 1,500,000. Thus, the file size is reduced to one-fourth (not one-half) of the original.

(2) **Lowering the bit depth:**

The bit depth determines the number of distinct colors available in your image. The available options of bit depth given to you during capturing depend on your scanner or digital camera. At the time of writing this chapter, the most common bit depth for color digital images is 24 bits. The 48-bit option is also available.

As shown in the file size calculation for a 6-megapixel, 24-bit image, the bit depth is multiplied by the total number of pixels. This means that the file size is directly proportional to the bit depth. For example, reducing the bit depth from 24 bits to 8 bits will reduce the file size to one-third of the original. Depending on the content of your image, lowering the bit depth from 24 bits to 8 bits may produce a very noticeable degradation of the image's aesthetics. Lowering the bit depth from 48 bits to 24 bits will reduce the file size to half but the degradation of the image may not be as noticeable.

WEIGHING BIT DEPTH AGAINST FILE SIZE

A color depth of 24 bits allows 2^{24} (i.e., 16,777,216) colors—about 16 million colors; 8 bits allows 2^8 (i.e., 256) colors. In reducing 24-bit to 8-bit color depth, you can reduce the file size to one-third. However, you reduce the number of colors from 16,777,216 to 256. That is, you lose more than 16 million allowable colors in the image—this is about a factor of 65,000 decrease—to trade for a factor of 3 decrease in file size.

On the other hand, some images do not need more than 256 colors. You do not have to keep a higher bit depth than the image needs.

- Grayscale images, such as scanned images of black-and-white photos and handwritten notes in pen or pencil, can have a bit depth of 8 bits without much noticeable degradation in image quality.
- Some handwritten notes even may be reduced to 2-bit or 1-bit color depth.
- An illustration graphic, such as a poster or logo, that contains only a few colors as large areas of solid colors can benefit from a lower bit depth. If you capture these graphics, whether by scanning or digital photography, solid colors (such as in Figure 10) will become continuous tones. In this case, if you consolidate all these slightly different colors into the one single color it is supposed to be, you may be able to reduce the bit depth, thus reducing the file size. The additional advantage of doing so is that the resulting digital image actually will be more faithful to the large areas of solid colors in the original analog source.

Figure 10 A 24-bit scanned image from a book cover has a supposedly solid blue background. The zoomed-in view would show that it is now made up of many slightly different colors although the differences may not show up well here in a printed copy.

FILE SIZES OF DIGITAL IMAGES

In a 24-bit color image, you use 8 bits to store each of the red, green, and blue components. In principle, with the same pixel dimensions, the file size of a 24-bit image file is three times as large as that for a grayscale image (8-bit). The following exercises will help you confirm your answer.

Activity/Exercise

If you have access to Adobe Photoshop, create a new file of 12 × 10 pixels. Convert the image to grayscale by selecting Image > Mode > Grayscale. Save the image as a RAW file format by selecting File > Save As . . . . In the Save dialog box, choose Photoshop Raw (*.RAW) for the file format, and name the file grayscale.raw. What do you think the file size of this grayscale.raw is?

> Check out the file size.
> (For Windows: Right-click on the file and choose Properties.)
> (For Mac: Select the file and hit Command-I.)
> **Answer:** The file size of grayscale.raw is 120 bytes (12 × 10 pixels, and each pixel uses 1 byte [8 bits] to hold its gray value).

Now convert the original image to 24-bit color by selecting Image > Mode > RGB Color. Save the image as rgb.raw. What do you think the file size of this rgb.raw is?

> Check out the file size.
> **Answer:** The file size of rgb.raw is 360 bytes (12 × 10 pixels × 3 bytes per pixel; 1 byte for red color information, 1 for green, and 1 for blue.)

In a raw file, 1 byte is used for each pixel in a grayscale picture, and 3 bytes are used for each pixel in a 24-bit image. What if you save the image as another format, such as .PSD, .BMP, or .TIF? The file size changes because the other file formats may embed additional image information in the file, such as dimensions. (Try opening in Adobe Photoshop the .raw file you have created. Notice that it prompts you for the pixel dimensions of the image and other information. But it does not prompt you for such information if you are opening a .PSD or a .BMP file.) In addition, some file formats are compressed using image compression algorithms. Therefore, unlike raw files, the file sizes for the image files in these different formats are difficult to predict by doing simple math. However, it is generally true that the following factors will increase the file size of a digital image:

- Larger pixel dimensions of the image
- Higher bit depth

(3) **Compressing the file:**

Compression is a method for reducing the size of a file by squeezing the same information into fewer bits. In a lossless compression algorithm, no information is lost. In a lossy compression algorithm, some information is lost. Lossy algorithms, however, are usually designed so that the information to be left out is the information that the human sensory system is not sensitive to anyway.

When you choose a format in which to save a digital image, you are implicitly choosing whether and how to compress the file. When you scan in a picture, you might be given the option of opening it with an image editing program or saving it as a

TIFF file, bitmapped picture, JPEG file, or GIF file. The file type is identified by a suffix on the file name: .tif or .tiff for a TIFF file, .bmp for a bitmapped picture, .jpg or .jpeg for a JPEG file, and .gif for a Graphics Interchange Format.

Generally, when working with digital images, it is best to keep the image in an uncompressed format. If you want to compress the image when you are still in the editing stage, you should use only a lossless compression method. For example, you can scan a color picture in as a TIFF file and open it in an image editing program to work on its tonal adjustment, contrast, color enhancement, refinements, and composition. After you have made the desired changes, you should save a copy of this final image either uncompressed or with lossless compression. When you are ready to save the image for distribution, you can choose a different file type with compression, even lossy, as is suitable for the intended use of the image. The file format depends on the type and use of the picture. For the Web, you can save the image as a JPEG, GIF, or PNG file. In the case of JPEG files, you also can choose the extent to which you want the file compressed, trading off image quality for a file size that is suitable for your needs.

AN EXAMPLE OF LOSSLESS COMPRESSION

More extensive coverage of the RLE algorithm and other compression algorithms can be found in the CS Module of this series.

Run-length encoding (RLE) is an example of a simple lossless compression algorithm. In this method, a sequence of the same repeated value is replaced by one instance of the value followed by the number of times it is repeated. For example, suppose that a blue color is represented in 8 bits as 00001010. If there is a section of sky in a digital image where blue is repeated for 100 pixels, then with no compression this section would take up 800 bits. With run-length encoding, this section could be encoded as one instance of blue—00001010—followed by the number 100 in binary (01100100). Instead of 800 bits, it now uses 16 bits.

This type of compression is used in .bmp files. For example, the file size of an uncompressed .bmp file of 100×100 pixels is 11,080 bytes. If the image contains only one single color, the file size can be reduced to 1,480 bytes with RLE compression. If the image contains two color blocks (Figure 11), the file size is 1,680 bytes with RLE compression.

Yue-Ling Wong

Figure 11 A bitmapped image containing two color blocks.

7 COLOR REPRESENTATION

Color models are used to describe colors numerically, usually in terms of varying amounts of primary colors. Each model uses a different method and a set of primaries to describe colors. The most common color models are RGB, CMYK, HSB, and CIE and their variants.

7.1 RGB Color Model

In the **RGB color model**, the three primary colors are red, green, and blue. Red light added with green light gives yellow; green and blue gives cyan; blue and red gives magenta (Figure 12). Adding full intensity of all red, green, and blue light gives white. This model is appropriate to the physiology of the human eye, which has receptors for the three components.

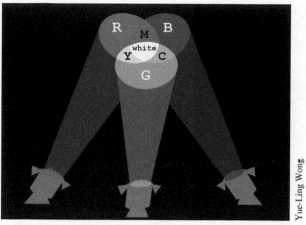

Figure 12 RGB: An additive color system. ▦ This image can be found on the insert.

THE HUMAN EYE'S RESPONSE TO COLOR

The wavelengths of visible light range from about 380 to 700 nm (nanometers)—creating a continuous spectrum of rainbow color, from the violet end (380 nm) to the red end (700 nm). A particular wavelength in this spectrum corresponds to a particular color.

The retina of the human eye has two categories of light receptors: rods and cones. Rods are active in dim light but have no color sensitivity. Cones are active in bright light and have color sensitivity. There are three types of cones. Roughly speaking, one type is sensitive to red, one to green, and one to blue. They are designated by Greek letters *rho* (ρ), *gamma* (γ), and *beta* (β), respectively. The curves representing the relative sensitivity of these three receptors for the normal human eye are shown in Figure 13. The γ and β cone types correspond quite closely to green and blue regions.

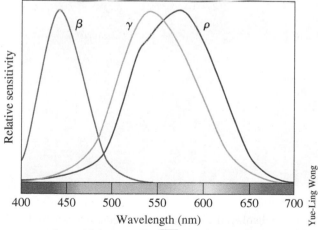

Figure 13 Human spectral sensitivity to color. ▦ This image can be found on the insert.

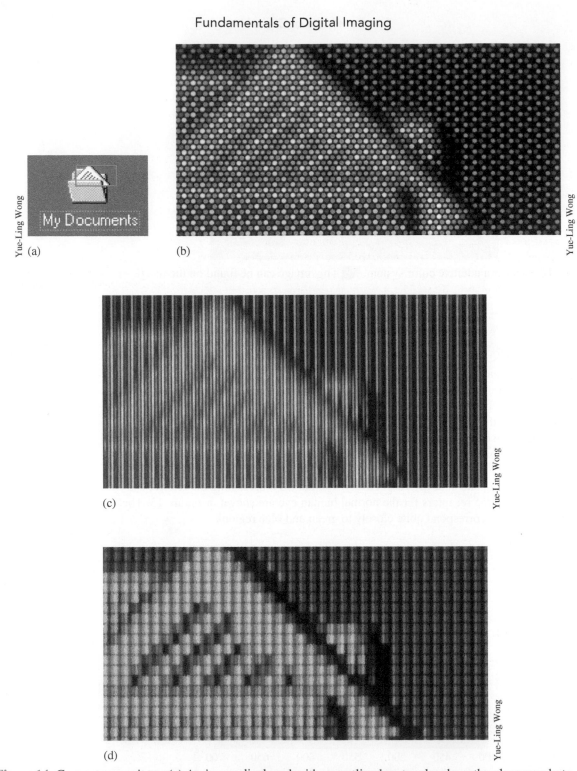

Figure 14 Computer monitors: (a) An image displayed with an outlined rectangle where the close-up photographs (b) through (d) were taken. (b) Close-up of a standard monitor screen. (c) Close-up view of a SONY Trinitron monitor screen. (d) Close-up view of an LCD display. ▚ This image can be found on the insert.

For computer monitors, colors are represented by points of light. They can be designed so that each pixel's color results from combined beams of red, green, and blue light. Computers are therefore based on an ***additive color system***, where the more colored light is blended in, the higher the overall light intensity. The close-up views of two CRT monitors and an LCD display shown in the color insert for Figure 14 show the dots and bands of red, green, and blue light. Despite the different shapes and patterns of the light spots used in the different displays, each pixel's color of the image is displayed by combined beams of red, green, and blue light of various intensity.

The RGB color model can be depicted graphically as a cube defined by three axes in 3-D space, as illustrated in Figure 15. The x-axis represents the red values, the y-axis the green values, and the z-axis the blue values. The origin (0, 0, 0) of the RGB color cube corresponds to black because all three colors have zero intensity. The corners of the cube correspond to red, green, blue, and their complementary colors—cyan, magenta, and yellow—respectively. The corresponding 24-bit RGB color mode in digital image editing programs allows values ranging from 0 to 255 for each of the three components, which also is referred to as a channel. Each channel uses 8 bits. In this case, white has an RGB value of (255, 255, 255). An RGB value of (255, 166, 38) is a light orange color.

> ⤏ **RGB Color Cube** An interactive tutorial lets you select a color and display its location in the 3-D space of the RGB color cube. You can drag to rotate the color cube to examine the color location.

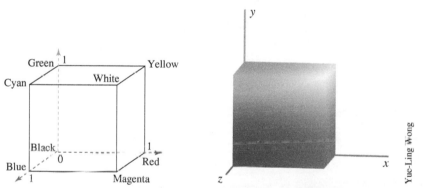

Figure 15 An illustration of the RGB color cube. ▄▄ This image can be found on the insert.

CORRELATING RGB COLOR CUBE WITH COLOR PICKERS

If you have worked with digital image editing programs such as Adobe Photoshop, you should have worked with color pickers like the one shown in Figure 16.

The color picker is often represented as a 2-D plane made up with gradients of colors. If you choose one of the R, G, or B components in the color picker, the vertical color slider displays the range of color for that component (0 is at the bottom of the slider and 255 is at the top). The 2-D plane next to the slider is a color field that displays all the colors that have the same R value but with varying values of other two color components, which are represented as the x- and y-axes. For example, if you click the red component (R), the color slider displays the range of color for red. A circle on the color field corresponds to the current selected color. This color has the red value equal to the selected

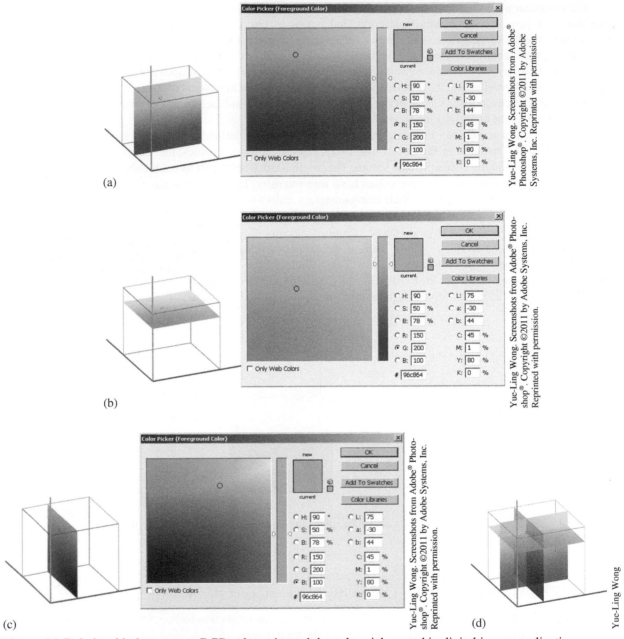

Figure 16 Relationship between an RGB color cube and the color picker used in digital image applications. This image can be found on the insert.

value on the color slider. Its green and blue values correspond to the x and y coordinates of the circle on the color field.

The RGB value is a 3-D coordinate of that color within the 3-D space of the cube. The color field is only a rectangular slice from the RGB color cube. Let's take a color with an RGB value of (150, 200, 100) as an example. If you click on the R component, the color field is a 2-D slice from the RGB color cube at R = 150 (Figure 16a) with the green axis as the *y*-axis and the blue axis as the *x*-axis. All the colors on this color field has the red value of 150. This works analogously for the selection of the G and B components (Figures 16b and 16c).

As you see in Figure 16, the same color can be found on three different color fields or slices. You see one color field at a time in Photoshop's color picker. The choice of the color axis determines which color field is displayed in the color picker. If you imagine that all three slices are showing in the color cube, they intersect at a single point in space (Figure 16d). The 3-D coordinate of this intersection point is the RGB value of the selected color.

7.2 CMYK Color Model

At some point in your art education, you may have been told that you could create nearly any color by mixing red, yellow, and blue painting media—crayons, watercolor, oil paint, or acrylics. These three colors are the primary colors in a *subtractive color model*. The model is subtractive because the more color pigment you layer on top or mix together, the more light you subtract out. Therefore, in theory, layering or mixing equal amounts of all three primaries should give you black.

> ⎙ Color Value Appraisal Be a "color value appraiser" and see how accurately you can estimate a color's "color value" in RGB.

In the *CMYK color model*, the three primaries are magenta, yellow, and cyan (Figure 17) instead of red, yellow, and blue. CMYK stands for cyan, magenta, yellow, and black. Mixing cyan with magenta gives blue; magenta with yellow gives red; and yellow with cyan gives green. In theory, mixing cyan, magenta, and yellow produces black. The CMY are the colors that are complementary to red, green, and blue, respectively. This means that mixing cyan with red gives black. This is the same for mixing magenta with green or yellow with blue.

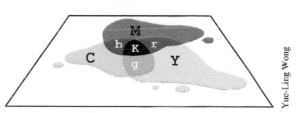

Figure 17 CMYK: A subtractive color system. In theory, mixing cyan, magenta, and yellow gives black. ▪▪ This image can be found on the insert.

The printing process is essentially a subtractive process, and CMYK is a subtractive color model. When one ink is added on top of another, it can effectively cause its complementary color not to be reflected. In that sense, the color is being subtracted out. Each of these components is specified in percentages.

In theory, (100%, 100%, 100%) gives black. In practice, due to the imperfections in the inks, (100%, 100%, 100%) actually gives a rather muddy brownish kind of black, not a deep black. The last component, K (black), is added to overcome this problem. In addition, using black ink in place of equal amounts of the three color inks is also a cost-effective choice.

7.3 HSB Color Model

Although RGB corresponds well to the technology of computer displays and the physiology of the human eye, it is not necessarily the most natural way for us to think about color. When you have a color in mind, you would probably describe it in terms of its hue first, such as a color found in a rainbow. Then, you would describe its brightness. However, it is not intuitive to think in terms of how much of each of the red, green, and blue components makes up the color.

An alternative to RGB is to specify a color by its hue, saturation, and brightness:

- **Hue** is the basic color based on the colors in a rainbow.
- **Saturation** is the intensity or purity of the color—essentially how far away from the neutral gray of the same brightness. As a color's saturation value decreases, it looks more washed out until eventually it becomes the neutral gray of the corresponding brightness.
- **Brightness** defines the lightness or darkness of the color. The lower the brightness value of a color is, the more it moves toward black.

This model matches well with the way humans intuitively think about colors. The **HSB** (or HSV) **color model** is this type of model, as is the HSL (or HLS) model. There are some differences between the mathematical representations of HSL and HSB, but they are built upon the same concepts of hue, saturation, and brightness.

As shown in Figure 18a, the HSB or HSV model looks like an inverted pyramid or cone with six sides—a hexacone. Arranged on a color wheel (Figure 18c) is a spectrum of color from red, yellow, green, cyan, blue, to purple and back to red.

- The color or the hue (H) is expressed as a degree between 0° (starting from red) and 360° (back to red again) to indicate its location on a color wheel in the order of the colors in a rainbow.
- The saturation (S) is expressed in the percentage of distance from the center of the color wheel. The color at the center of the color wheel is a fully desaturated color—a gray color of the corresponding brightness.

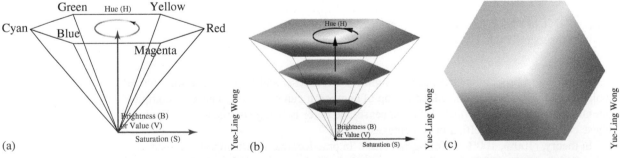

Figure 18 (a) Hexacone of the HSB or HSV color model. (b) Hexacone with selected slices at different levels of brightness or value. (c) A slice of the color wheel from the HSB or HSV color model. ■ This image can be found on the insert.

- The vertical axis is the brightness (B) or value (V). The higher the brightness or value is, the lighter the color. For example, at B = 0%, the color is black no matter what the values for saturation and hue are. At B = 100%, all colors are at their brightest. White is located at the center of the color wheel at B = 100%.

> ✎ **RGB Color Cube to HSV** A QuickTime movie illustrating the relationship between the RGB color cube and the HSV hexacone.

HSB VERSUS HSL

HSL stands for hue, saturation, and luminance. The HSL color model is similar to the HSB model. In HSL, the most saturated colors can be found at L = 50%, which is compared to B = 100% in the HSB color model (Figure 19). At L = 0%, the color is black no matter what the hue and saturation are. Unlike the HSB color model, the color at L = 100% in HSL is white no matter what the hue and saturation are.

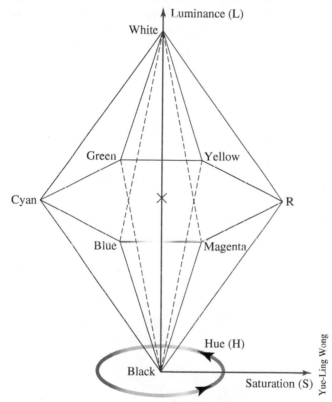

Figure 19 HSL color model.

7.4 CIE XYZ

In 1931, the Commission Internationale d'Eclairage (CIE) worked out a color system to encompass all of the colors that are visible to average humans. It uses three "virtual primaries" designated as X, Y, and Z. These primaries are not any physical colors. With these primaries as the base, it is possible to graphically depict a color gamut to encompass all visible colors.

The CIE color model has evolved into new variants, but it is still the standard to which all other color models are compared, because its color space encompasses all of the colors humans can see.

COLOR GAMUTS: VISIBLE COLORS, RGB, AND CMYK

A chromaticity diagram, as illustrated in Figure 20, often is used to define, compare, and explain *color gamuts* and *color spaces*. Color gamut refers to the range of colors that a specific system can produce or capture. Color space is defined by a color gamut and a color model that is used to describe the colors.

The given diagram is constructed based on the CIE XYZ color space. The colors encompassed in the horseshoe shape include all the colors visible to humans. The boundary line of this horseshoe shape follows the visible color spectrum. Because no printing device can output all of the visible colors, the colors you see in the color insert of this figure only give you a rough idea of the distribution of colors within this color space.

Figure 20 is used here to show you a comparison of RGB and CMYK color gamuts. As you see, the combination of the R, G, and B light sources cannot duplicate the full gamut of human vision.

Note that although the CMYK gamut is smaller than the RGB gamut, some CMYK colors are outside of the RGB gamut.

CMYK printers normally have smaller gamuts (Figure 20c) than RGB monitors (Figure 20b). When printing a digital image, the colors that are out of the color gamut of the printer are mapped to other colors within the printer's color gamut. Note that the three corners of the RGB color gamut that contain the most saturated colors are outside of the CMYK gamut. This means that those highly saturated colors in your digital images may look bright and saturated on your computer but may appear a little duller when printed from an inkjet printer or an offset printer in a professional print shop. Printers with more than four colors (such as 6-color printers with additional light cyan and light magenta) can have larger gamuts.

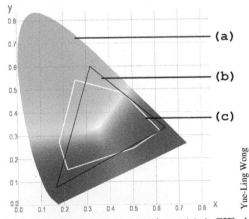

Figure 20 An illustration for color gamut comparison: (a) A CIE chromaticity diagram. (b) RGB color gamut of typical CRT monitors. The exact shape of the device's color space depends on the monitor's red, green, and blue phosphors. Note that this does not include all the colors humans can see. (c) CMYK color gamut of typical inkjet printers. The exact shape of the color space depends on the colorants of the printer's ink. ▄▟ This image can be found on the insert.

7.5 Other Color Models

When working with digital images, you also may see a reference to the L*a*b*, YUV, or YIQ color models. These color models divide color into one luminance (brightness) component and two chrominance (color) components.

The YUV or YIQ models are not used in image editing, but you may read about them with regard to JPEG image compression, video standard, and television transmission. Originally, both the YUV and YIQ models were found to be useful in television transmission (when color TV was invented), because these models separate out the information needed for black-and-white transmission (all contained in the Y component) from that needed for color. The same signal could then be used for both types of television. YUV was originally the color model for video transmission in Europe under the PAL standard. YIQ is the model adopted by the National Television System Committee (NTSC) in the United States.

The advantages of the YIQ and YUV models in data compression have to do with the way the human eye perceives color. Human vision is more sensitive to differences in luminance than differences in chrominance. Thus, it is possible to reduce the amount of detail in the chrominance information by using a smaller data size for these components. This makes the image data more compact in size.

You may encounter the L*a*b* color model in your work with digital images. Like YUV and YIQ, this model has one luminance component (L*) and two chrominance components (a* ranging from green to red, and b* ranging from blue to yellow). Based on the original CIE model, L*a*b* has the advantage of allowing you to create device-independent colors. That is, with L*a*b* and proper calibration of the devices (displays and printers), you can ensure that the color you see on your computer will be faithfully reproduced on another computer display and printer—assuming that the colors are within the gamut for the device.

8 COLOR MODES

When you work in an image editing program, there are choices of color modes. For example, the color modes available in Photoshop include RGB color, CMYK color, Lab color, grayscale, bitmap, Duotone, indexed color, and Multichannel. You use one color mode at a time for your image file, but you can switch between different color modes during the image editing process.

Some color modes in digital image processing programs are based on the color models, but color modes differ from color models. Color modes specify which color model is used to display and print the image you're working on. They also determine the number of colors and the number of channels for the image you are working on.

For example, there are three channels in the RGB color mode—one for red, one for green, and one for blue. In most situations, each channel's default color depth is 8 bits, making the RGB mode 24 bits ($2^{24} = 16,777,216$ colors) in this case. In the grayscale color mode, there is only one channel. By default, the channel's color depth is 8 bits ($2^8 = 256$ colors).

The choice of color mode depends on the nature and intent of the digital image you are working on. Generally, you work and save your original images files in RGB mode. However, CMYK generally is used for images that are to be printed. If you are preparing a digital image for full-color offset printing, it is best to use the CMYK color mode. However, some inkjet printers recommend RGB color mode. If your image is intended for the Web, then you should stay in RGB mode.

You can switch between different color modes during the image editing process. However, switching from one color mode to another may cause loss of original color information, because each mode has different color gamuts. The out-of-gamut colors will be altered to fit within the new gamut.

COLOR GAMUTS BETWEEN RGB AND CMYK COLOR MODES

Activities/Exercises

The objectives of these activities are to demonstrate that: (1) the most saturated colors within the RGB color gamut are outside of the CMYK gamut (as illustrated in Figure 20) and (2) switching between color modes may result in loss of the original color information of the image.

Activity 1: Switching from RGB Color Mode to CMYK Color Mode

1. Create a new Photoshop image in RGB color mode.
2. Create three solid blocks of most saturated red, green, and blue with RGB values of (255,0,0), (0,255,0), and (0,0,255), respectively.
3. Switch to CMYK color mode.

You will see these three colors become a little washed out.

If you switch back to RGB color mode, the colors will not be reverted to the original. If you check the color information of these colors using the eyedropper tool, you will see that the RGB values of these three colors are altered. They are not (255,0,0), (0,255,0), and (0,0,255) anymore.

Activity 2: Switching from CMYK Color Mode to RGB Color Mode

1. Create a new Photoshop image in CMYK color mode.
2. Create three solid blocks of most saturated cyan, magenta, and yellow with CMYK values of (100%,0,0,0), (0,100%,0,0), and (0,0,100%,0), respectively.
3. Switch to RGB color mode, then switch back to CMYK color mode.

If you check the color information of these colors using the eyedropper tool, you will see that the CMYK values of these three colors are altered. Note that the cyan color has the most significant change. Recall that, as shown in Figure 20, the cyan area of the CMYK color gamut is outside of the RGB gamut.

INDEXED COLOR

An additional color mode available in digital image processing programs is *indexed color*. It is a technique for limiting the number of representable colors to no more than 256 (8-bit) based on those actually used in the image. The colors used in the image are stored as a palette called a *color lookup table (CLUT)*. Each color in the table is assigned a number or an index. The index number starts with zero. The color information of each

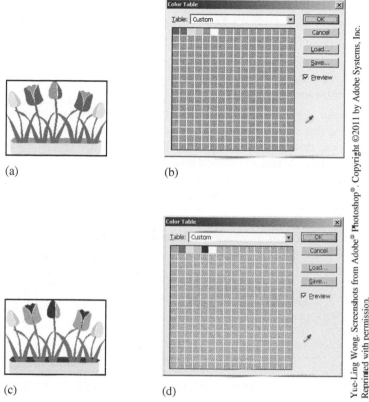

(a)

(b)

(c)

(d)

Figure 21 (a) An image using indexed colors. (b) The color table or palette for the indexed colors. (c) The image with changes made to the indexed colors. (d) The color table that is used by the image in (c). ▄▄ This image can be found on the insert.

pixel in the image is stored as a color number from the palette. This is analogous to paint-by-number art kits.

If the color of a particular index number in the palette is altered, all of the pixels in the image using the color of that index will be changed to the new color. The color is changed, but the index number remains the same. As you see in Figure 21, you can change the color in an indexed color image just by changing the color on the color table or applying a different color table to the same image.

The color table in Figure 21b consists of six colors (See the color insert). The color number 0, which is the first color on the table, is a red color. The index for the sixth color, which is white, is 5. In Figure 21c the red and orange tulips now become blue by altering the color 0 from a red to a light blue and color 4 from an orange to a dark blue. The base of the tulip changes from orange to the new dark blue, too, because the pixels in that area have the color index of 4. The color numbers assigned to the pixels in the image remain the same. The color table shown in Figure 21d shows the changes of color of indexes 0 and 4.

ALTERING COLORS IN CLUT

Activity/Exercise

The objectives of this activity are to demonstrate: (1) how to check out the CLUT of an indexed-color image in Photoshop, and (2) how changing the color in the CLUT can alter the color in the image.

1. Open a color image in Photoshop. An image with big blocks of distinct solid colors, such as the one shown in Figure 21, will work best for the purpose of this activity. You also can download the sample file (Figure 21a) from the Web site of this text or create a new file and add several blocks of colors.

2. Convert the image to indexed color mode: `Image > Mode > Indexed Color...` For the purpose of this activity, any settings for `Palette` and `Forced` should work (Figure 22).

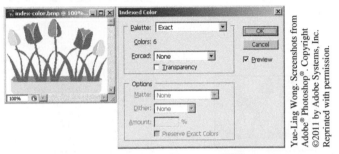

Figure 22 An image is converted to indexed-color mode. ▄▄ This image can be found on the insert.

If your image has more than 256 colors, you will see the option `Dither`. Make sure to set the `Dither` option to None. This will help you see the changes you are going to make in the next steps.

3. Check out the color table for this indexed-color image: `Image > Color Table...` You should see a color table similar to Figure 21b. Depending on your image, there may be different colors and different number of colors in your table.

4. Try to click on a color square in the color table and change it to a different color. You will see all the areas in the image that use this color change to the new color, as in Figure 23.

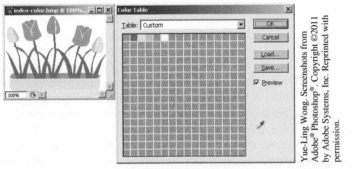

Figure 23 The first color (index 0) on the color table is changed to a light blue. ▄▄ This image can be found on the insert.

9 DIFFICULTIES IN REPRODUCING COLORS IN DIGITAL IMAGES

There are at least two common problems in reproducing colors in digital images:

(1) **Digital devices cannot produce all of the colors visible to humans.**

Human vision has a larger gamut than the current existing digital devices can produce. The term *gamut* refers to the range of colors a specific system can produce or capture. The combination of R, G, and B phosphors of a computer display cannot create all the colors humans can see. Printers use the CMYK system, which has even smaller gamuts than the RGB system used for computer displays (Figure 20).

(2) **Difficulties exist in reproducing color across devices.**

The CMYK system used in printing is a subtractive color system, whereas the RGB system used in computer displays is an additive color system. The colors in digital images may not be reproduced exactly, whether from computer displays to printers or even from one computer display to another computer display. Although computer displays and other RGB devices use RGB color models, not all of them can produce the exact same range of colors. Different devices have different color gamuts and color spaces.

COLOR SPACES

Color spaces differ from color models. A color model is a theoretical system that describes colors numerically in terms of primary colors or components. The primary components defined in a color model are used as the model's dimensional coordinates. For example, the RGB color model describes colors in terms of red, green, and blue values. A color space refers to a collection of colors that can be produced based on a color model.

When you work with colors of a digital image in an image editing program, you are adjusting numerical values in the file. These numerical values are not associated with absolute colors. For example, a red color with an RGB value of (255, 0, 0) may appear as different shades of red on different monitors and on prints from different printers. What specific color the numeric value means depends on the color space of the device that produces that color. The numeric value is interpreted by the color space of the device that is reproducing that color. The CIE XYZ color space usually is used as the reference color space for those colors, because it encompasses all of the colors visible to humans.

Example color spaces are Adobe RGB and sRGB. Both are based on the RGB model and have a triangular shape like the RGB one shown in Figure 20. Adobe RGB has a larger color space than sRGB. sRGB is recommended for Web images for onscreen viewing because sRGB defines the color space of the standard monitor.

IDENTIFYING OUT-OF-GAMUT COLORS

Out-of-gamut colors are not reproduced correctly. In digital image editing programs such as Adobe Photoshop, you can tell whether a color is out of gamut based on your CMYK setting. In the Photoshop color picker and the color palette, you will see a warning symbol (Figure 24).

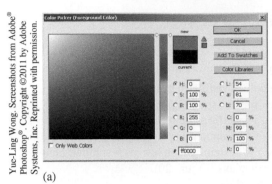
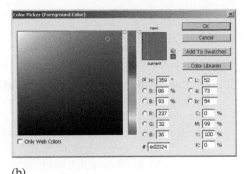

(a)   (b)

Figure 24 Adobe Photoshop color picker showing an example of the out-of-gamut colors. (a) The red color has the saturation S = 100% and RGB = (255, 0, 0). Note the exclamation mark icon ⚠ next to the color chip. It is a warning of out of gamut for printing. Clicking on the icon ⚠ gives the closest color in gamut for printing. (b) Note the new RGB and HSB values of this new color.

> ✎ Concept of Color Management
> Supplementary reading on the difficulties in reproducing colors across devices and the concepts of color management.

A *color management system (CMS)* is a software solution intended to help reproduce colors across different devices—digital cameras, scanners, computer displays, and printers—in a predictable and reproducible way by reading and translating colors between the color gamuts of these different devices.

10 SUMMARY

Our vision of the world around us is inherently an analog phenomenon. Theoretically, an infinite number of color shades and tones is possible, and points of color in space are infinite because between every two points there is another. Because of the discrete and finite nature of computers, the analog information of natural images needs to be digitized in order to be stored on computers. Digitization involves a two-step process—sampling and quantizing.

The sampling step is to record discrete point samples on an image plane. The point sample is called a picture element, or pixel for short. Each pixel stores the color information of the corresponding position in the image. The position is defined by its horizontal and vertical coordinates in the image.

The sampling rate defines how frequently you take a sample. Imagine a two-dimensional grid is applied on the image and a single color sample is obtained from each tiny cell on the grid. The higher the sampling rate, the finer the grid and the more samples or pixels you will have in the digital image—that is, the higher the image resolution.

The quantizing step is to map an infinite number of colors and shades to a finite number of colors. The number of colors in this finite set is defined by the bit depth.

Increasing the sampling rate or bit depth increases the file size of the image. For an uncompressed file, doubling the sampling rate or the bit depth can double the file size.

Sampling and quantization errors are unavoidable results of the discrete, finite nature of digital media. It is not possible to create a digital version of a photograph or a real-world scene that has absolute fidelity to the original image. However, the human eye is not infinitely sensitive to differences in colors and color gradations across space, so it turns out that digital representations of pictures are often more than adequate for re-creations of what we see in the world.

Color models are used to describe colors numerically, usually in terms of varying amounts of primary colors. Each model uses a different method and a set of primaries to describe colors. The most common color models are RGB, CMYK, HSB, and CIE and their variants.

Color modes in digital image processing programs generally are based on the color models. Your choice of color mode in an image processing program depends on the nature and intent of a digital image. In general, you work on and save your original source files in RGB mode. If your digital image is for print, you can always convert the file to CMYK as needed. Keep in mind that CMYK has a smaller gamut, and thus switching from RGB to CMYK may cause some loss of colors. Some inkjet printers, though using CMYK inks, recommend that you keep the images in RGB mode. If your image is intended for the Web, then you should stay in RGB mode.

TERMS

24 bits	color lookup table	pixel dimensions
32-bit	(CLUT)	quantization
additive color system	color management system	raster graphics
aliasing	(CMS)	rasterize
anti-aliasing	color space	resolution
bit depth	HSB color model	RGB color model
bitmapped	hue	sampling
brightness	indexed color	saturation
CMYK color model	megapixel	subtractive color
color depth	picture element	model
color gamut	pixel	vector graphics

LEARNING AIDS

The following learning aids can be found at the text's companion Web site.

🖰 **Sampling and Quantizing in Digital Images**
An interactive tutorial, complementary to the materials covered in Sections 2.1 and 2.2, explaining sampling and quantizing in digitizing an image.

🖰 **Pegboard and Resolution**
An interactive tutorial using the pegboard as an analogy to explain resolution in capturing and displaying digital images.

🖰 **RGB Color Cube**
An interactive tutorial that lets you select a color and display its location in the 3-D space of the RGB color cube. You can drag to rotate the color cube to examine the color location.

🖰 **Color Value Appraisal**
Be a "color value appraiser" and see how accurately you can estimate a color's "color value" in RGB.

◈ **RGB Color Cube to HSV**

A QuickTime movie illustrating the relationship between the RGB color cube and the HSV hexacone.

◈ **Concept of Color Management**

Supplementary reading on the concepts of color management and difficulties in reproducing colors across devices.

REVIEW QUESTIONS

When applicable, please select all correct answers.

1. The process of converting from analog to digital information is a two-step process—sampling and quantizing. In converting an analog image to a digital image, the sampling rate affects _____.

   A. the bit depth of the resulting digital image
   B. the pixel dimensions of the resulting digital image

2. The process of converting from analog to digital information is a two-step process—sampling and quantizing. In the quantization step, to convert an analog image to a digital image, _____.

   A. a two-dimensional grid is applied on the image and each tiny cell on the grid is converted into a pixel
   B. a two-dimensional grid is applied on the image to apply dithering to the image
   C. an infinite number of color shades and tones in an analog image is mapped to a finite set of discrete color values
   D. the resulting digital image file is compressed to have a smaller file size

3. Which of the following factors will increase the file size of a digital image?

   A. Larger pixel dimensions of the image
   B. Higher color depth

4. A digital image captured at a higher resolution _____ than it would have if it had been captured at a lower resolution.

   A. captures more details
   B. has more different colors
   C. has a higher bit depth
   D. has a larger file size
   E. has larger pixel dimensions
   F. uses a higher sampling rate

5. A digital image captured at a higher bit depth _____ than it would have if it had been captured at a lower bit depth.

   A. captures more details
   B. has more different colors
   C. has a larger file size
   D. has larger pixel dimensions
   E. uses a higher sampling rate

6. The term *pixel* is contracted from the words _____ and _____.

7. **True/False**: A pixel is a point sample, not a little square.

8. **True/False**: An 1-bit color depth allows only black and white colors.

9. An 1-bit color depth allows _____ colors.

10. An 8-bit color depth allows _____ colors.

11. A 24-bit color depth allows _____ colors.

12. Bitmapped images are composed of _____.

    A. individual pixels, which represent spatial samples of the image or scene
    B. mathematical descriptions of image elements, which include points, lines, curves, and shapes

13. Vector graphics are composed of _____.

    A. individual pixels, which represent spatial samples of the image or scene
    B. mathematical descriptions of image elements, which include points, lines, curves, and shapes

14. The main advantage(s) of bitmapped images over vector graphics is (are) _____.

    A. scalability or resolution independence of images
    B. ease of editing the image content pixel by pixel
    C. more compact file size compared to vector graphics

15. The main advantage(s) of vector graphics over bitmapped images is (are) _____.

    A. scalability or resolution independence of images
    B. ease of editing the image content pixel by pixel
    C. more compact file size compared to bitmapped images

16. Sometimes when you magnify a picture on your computer screen, lines that should be straight lines appear to be jagged. This effect is called _____.

    A. anti-aliasing
    B. aliasing
    C. dithering
    D. indexing

17. Generally speaking, how does the file size change if the total number of pixels of an image is doubled?

18. Generally speaking, how does the file size change if the number of pixels of both the width and height of an image are doubled?

19. Generally speaking, how does the file size change if the bit depth of an image is increased from 8 bits to 16 bits?

20. Generally speaking, how does the file size change if the bit depth of an image is increased from 8 bits to 24 bits?

21. Give one example of the image file type that supports lossy compression and one that supports lossless compression.

22. Which of the following are file extensions of pixel-based files?

    BMP   DOC   JPEG   TXT   PNG   GIF
    JPG   PSD   TIFF   EPS   WMF

23. Which of the following are file extensions of vector graphic files?

BMP   DOC   JPEG   TXT   PNG   GIF   FLA

JPG   PSD   TIFF   EPS   WMF   SWF   AI

24. What are the primary colors in the RGB color model?

25. What are the primary colors in the CMY color model?

26. What are the primaries in the HSB color model?

27. Which of the following color models takes the form of a color cube?

A. RGB
B. CMY
C. HSB
D. CIE XYZ

28. Which of the following color models takes the form of a hexacone?

A. RGB
B. CMY
C. HSB
D. CIE XYZ

29. Which of the primaries in the HSB color model takes the form of a color wheel?

A. Hue
B. Saturation
C. Brightness

30. What is the color mixing method for the RGB color model?

A. Additive
B. Subtractive

31. What is the color mixing method for the CMY color model?

A. Additive
B. Subtractive

32. For the 24-bit color depth, what are the RGB values for (i) white, (ii) black, (iii) red, (iv) green, (v) blue, (vi) cyan, (vii) magenta, and (viii) yellow?

(You can use the color picker in your image editing program to confirm your answers.)

33. What are the theoretical CMY values for (i) white, (ii) black, (iii) red, (iv) green, (v) blue, (vi) cyan, (vii) magenta, and (viii) yellow?

34. What are the HSB values for (i) white, (ii) black, (iii) red, (iv) green, (v) blue, (vi) cyan, (vii) magenta, and (viii) yellow?

(You can use the color picker in your image editing program to confirm your answers.)

35. What is the primary use of the CMYK color model?

36. Why don't the colors in a printed image look exactly the same as those you see on the computer screen?

Capturing and Editing Digital Images

TABLE OF CONTENTS

courtesy of Yue-Ling Wong

Summary   Terms   Learning Aids   Review Questions

courtesy of Yue-Ling Wong

KEY CONCEPTS
- Working with scanners and scanning
- Digital photography
- Common tools in digital image editing programs—selection, layer, color and tonal adjustment, fine-tuning specific parts, sharpening
- Working with vector graphics programs
- Image ppi versus printer dpi
- Printing
- Images for the Web

GENERAL LEARNING OBJECTIVES

In this chapter, you will learn
- What scanning and printing resolution mean and how to determine them.
- The common tools of image editing and vector graphics programs.
- The general image editing processes.
- How to prepare images for the Web.

1 INTRODUCTION

The two commonly used methods for capturing digital images are scanning and digital photography. In this chapter, we will discuss types of scanners, common scanning options, and how to determine the optimal scanning resolution. This knowledge will help you capture digital images with an optimal quality that suits your expectations.

We will also have a brief discussion of digital cameras. Later in this chapter, we will cover topics on general digital image editing tools, how to determine the resolution for images that are to be printed, and how to optimize images created for the Web.

2 SCANNERS

Generally, there are four common types of scanners classified in terms of their mechanisms:
- *Flatbed scanners:* This versatile scanner is the one most commonly used for digital media labs, offices, and personal use. A flatbed usually can scan documents of letter size (8.5 × 11 inches), legal size (8.5 × 14 inches), or even 11 × 14 inches on its flat glass plate. The motorized scan head, which consists of a light source and arrays of sensors, is underneath the glass. The scan head moves from one end to the other to capture the image.

  Here is a general procedure for scanning a document with a flatbed scanner:
  1. Put the document face down on the glass plate.
  2. Align the document to the corner indicated on the scanner.

3. Close the flap cover.
4. Start the scanner software and preview the scanning. The scanner will scan the whole scanning area.
5. Select the region that you want if your document is smaller than the available scanning area.
6. Choose the scanning options—if available—such as color mode, resolution, sharpening level, histogram, and brightness/contrast adjustments. We will discuss these options in detail later in this chapter.
7. Finalize the scanning and save the file. There may be many different file formats available.

Some flatbed scanners also can be used to scan negatives or slides using a negative or slide adaptor. Digital artists also use flatbed scanners to scan 3-D objects, such as fabrics, keys, dried plants, and hands. In these cases, the flatbed scanner is used like a focus-free camera. When an object is scanned without the flatbed cover, the background appears black, allowing easy extraction of the object to compose with others in a project.

- *Sheet-fed scanners:* Many smaller portable scanners are sheet-fed scanners in which the document moves through a fixed scan head. Because of the feeding mechanism, this type of scanner is not able to scan thick objects, such as a page in a book. Sheetbed scanners are generally designed to scan no larger than letter-size paper.
- *Handheld scanners:* These scanners are also portable. The basic mechanism of handheld scanners is very similar to that of flatbeds, except that handhelds rely on the user to move the scan head. The scanning width of each pass is limited by the width of the device, which usually is less than the width of letter-size paper. For some models of handheld scanners, the image quality may rely on the user's steady hand movement. In general, handheld scanners do not provide very good image quality, but they offer the most convenient and fastest way of capturing documents. They are most useful for capturing text documents.
- *Drum scanners:* Drum scanners are capable of very high resolutions and can handle larger documents. They often are used in the publishing industry, where high-resolution images are required, or for scanning large documents, such as blueprints.

TWAIN

TWAIN is a standard or specification for the interface between image software and image capturing devices, such as scanners and digital cameras. Technically, TWAIN refers to an image-capture API (Application Programming Interface) for Microsoft Windows and Apple Mac OS. It is not a driver of any image-capturing devices.

The term TWAIN is not an acronym. The word was taken from the sentence "and never the twain shall meet" in Kipling's "The Ballad of East and West"—a fitting description of the challenges of connecting scanners to desktop computers in the early days of this technology. The whole word is capitalized to make it distinctive as a term. For more information, check out http://www.twain.org.

3 CAPTURING DIGITAL IMAGES BY SCANNING

One factor affecting the amount of detail in a scanned image is scanning resolution. Generally, the higher the resolution at which you scan the image, the more detail you can capture.

Advertisements for scanners often cite the high resolutions they offer. However, you should beware of these claims, as the term "resolution" can be used in two different ways with regard to scanners. In the scanner specification, you may find two numbers for resolution: one for the optical resolution and one for the enhanced or interpolated resolution.

The *optical resolution* is the hardware resolution, which is dependent on the number of sensors the scanner has to capture the image information. On the other hand, the *enhanced resolution* interpolates the image using software. The interpolation process increases the resolution by adding extra pixels to the ones that are actually captured by the sensors. Interpolated pixels are not truly or directly captured by the sensors. The color information of these extra pixels is based on the adjacent pixels. Many scanners now have unlimited software-enhanced resolution.

Scanner resolution is usually reported in *dpi (dots per inch)*. To understand what dpi is and what the practical meaning of this number is, let's consider the general mechanism of a scanner. A flatbed scanner has a moving scan head that contains an array of light sensors. The scan head moves across the scanner bed during scanning. Its movement is controlled by a stepper motor.

So, how is a picture—analog information—captured with only a row of light sensors? To answer this question, we must understand the concepts of sampling and sampling rate. The number of sensors available in this single row corresponds to the sampling rate in the x-direction. The discrete stepwise movement of the scan head is related to the sampling rate in the y-direction. The sensor corresponds to the *dot* in the unit dpi. Each sample results in a pixel of the scanned image. For example, many flatbed scanners now have an optical resolution of at least 2,400 dpi in each direction. If you scan a 1-inch $\times$ 1-inch picture at this scanning resolution, you will get an image of 2,400 $\times$ 2,400 pixels. A detailed discussion of how to determine optimal scanning resolution is in the following section.

3.1 Scanning Resolution Determination

For best results, you should scan at a high enough resolution (in dpi) to generate an image with sufficient pixels in each dimension. The scanning resolution is determined by how the scanned image will be used:

- If it is intended for printing, then what are the physical dimensions of the print going to be and what are the requirements of the printing device?
- If the final image is for the Web, then what are the required pixel dimensions of the image?

If the scan resolution is not set high enough to produce the required pixel dimensions, you may have to scale up the image later. However, scaling up an image will only add pixels by interpolating the color information already in the image. Using interpolation, you do not get additional picture details. The more you scale up an image, the blurrier it will appear. If you scan at a higher resolution than you need, you will need to resize down the image later. When you shrink an image by reducing its pixel dimensions, some pixels are removed; that is, you lose information. The color information of the remaining pixels is altered to fit the new size. Thus, it is best to use a scan resolution such that resizing the scanned image is minimal.

Intended for Web or Onscreen Display

If the final image is for Web or onscreen display, then its pixel dimensions are estimated relative to the screen resolution of the intended display device.

Capturing and Editing Digital Images

Suppose the screen resolution of your target audience is $1,280 \times 960$ pixels and you want your image to appear about half the width and height of the screen (i.e., the size of a quarter screen). This means that the resolution of your final image is about 640×480 pixels.

Intended for Print

If you plan to print out the scan, you will need to know the resolution requirements of the printing device in addition to the print size (in inches). You should always think of the scan in terms of the pixel dimensions, not the ppi or the physical print size (inches). Just like any digital images, scanned images do not possess any inherent physical dimensions. The physical dimensions materialize when the image is printed out, defined by both the image's pixel dimensions and the printing ppi.

The inch in the pixel per inch (ppi) and dots per inch (dpi) is in linear inches, not square inches.

The following equation shows the relationships among pixel dimensions, print dimensions, and print resolution:

$$\text{Pixel Dimensions (in pixels)} = \text{Print Dimensions (in inches)} \times \text{Print Resolution (in ppi)}$$

or,

$$\text{Print Dimensions (in inches)} = \frac{\text{Pixel Dimensions (in pixels)}}{\text{Print Resolution (in pixels per inch, ppi)}}$$

Let's see an example of determining the *print size* for a 2,400-pixel $\times$ 3,600-pixel image using the equations.

If this image is printed out on a printer at 600 ppi, then the print size will be 4×6.

$$\frac{2,400 \text{ pixels}}{600 \text{ ppi}} = 4 \text{ inches}$$

$$\frac{3,600 \text{ pixels}}{600 \text{ ppi}} = 6 \text{ inches}$$

If this same scan is printed out at 300 ppi, then the print will become 8×12.

$$\frac{2,400 \text{ pixels}}{300 \text{ ppi}} = 8 \text{ inches}$$

$$\frac{3,600 \text{ pixels}}{300 \text{ ppi}} = 12 \text{ inches}$$

If this same scan is printed out at 200 ppi, then the print will become 12×18.

$$\frac{2,400 \text{ pixels}}{200 \text{ ppi}} = 12 \text{ inches}$$

$$\frac{3,600 \text{ pixels}}{200 \text{ ppi}} = 18 \text{ inches}$$

These results, tabulated in Table 1, demonstrate that different sizes of prints can be made from the same scanned image by varying the print resolution.

In most situations when you scan a picture, you usually know the size you want for the final print of the scanned image. Now let's reverse the previous calculation process.

Suppose you want to scan a 1-inch $\times$ 1.5-inch area of a picture to make a 10-inch $\times$ 13-inch print (on the 11-inch $\times$ 14-inch paper) on an inkjet printer. To determine the scan resolution, you will first need to find out the pixel dimensions of the image you need. To find out the pixel dimensions, you need to know the print size and the print resolution.

TABLE I	Various Physical Dimensions, or Print Sizes, from an Image of the Same Pixel Dimensions	

| | | Pixel Dimensions | |
		2,400 pixels	3,600 pixels
Print Resolution	200 ppi	12 inches	18 inches
	300 ppi	8 inches	12 inches
	600 ppi	4 inches	6 inches

Let's step through the math for determining the scan resolution.

Step 1 **Determine the total pixels, or the pixel dimensions, of the final image**
Recall that:

$$\text{Pixel Dimensions (in pixels)} = \text{Print Dimensions (in inches)} \times \text{Print Resolution (in ppi)}$$

A print resolution of 150–300 ppi on an inkjet printer will give a good-quality print. Let's say you decide to print the image at 150 ppi. The pixel dimensions of a 10-inch × 13-inch image need to be 1,500 × 1,950 pixels.

$$10 \text{ inches} \times 150 \text{ ppi} = 1,500 \text{ pixels}$$
$$13 \text{ inches} \times 150 \text{ ppi} = 1,950 \text{ pixels}$$

Step 2 **Calculate the scan resolution (dpi)**
To calculate the scan resolution, you use a similar equation:

$$\text{Scan Resolution (in dpi)} = \frac{\text{Pixel Dimensions (in pixels)}}{\text{Scan Source Dimensions (in inches)}}$$

The scan source in this example is 1 inch by 1.5 inches. Therefore, the scan resolution can be calculated as follows.

$$\frac{1,500 \text{ pixels}}{1 \text{ inch}} = 1,500 \text{ ppi, or dpi (because each dot translates to a pixel in scanning)}$$

$$\frac{1,950 \text{ pixels}}{1.5 \text{ inch}} = 1,300 \text{ ppi, or dpi}$$

The discrepancy between the scan resolution calculations arises from the fact that the source picture and the target print have different width-to-height ratios, which is not an uncommon situation. But which calculated dpi should you use? In this example, no matter what resolution you choose, you will need to crop part of the image if you want the print to be exactly 10 inches × 13 inches.

If you are not sure whether you will crop the image to fit the exact size of 10 × 13, you should scan at the highest ppi calculated—in this case 1,500 dpi. Scanning at 1,500 dpi will give you an image of pixel dimensions of 2,250 × 1,500 pixels, which will be 10 inches × 15 inches if printed at 150 ppi. On the other hand, scanning at 1,300 dpi will give you an image of pixel dimensions of 1,300 × 1,950 pixels, which will give you an 8.7-inch × 13-inch print at 150 ppi print resolution.

Not all inkjet printers can print edge to edge or borderless. Depending on the printer, there are certain minimal margin requirements. In this example, although the image is intended to print on an 11-inch × 14-inch paper, we leave half an inch of margin on all four sides of the paper. Therefore, the dimensions of the image to be printed out are actually only 10 inches × 13 inches.

Exercise[*]: Verify that an image of 1,300 $\times$ 1,950 pixels will give you an 8.7-inch $\times$ 13-inch print when it is printed at 150 ppi.

3.2 Tonal Adjustments

Although you can perform color correction and editing after the scanning process, it is best to optimize the tonal range and correct any significant color problems during the scanning process. It is because once you have scanned the picture, any image editing you make to the image will be based on the color information you got from the scan. Editing the image later in an image editing program is not going to create any extra true color information. If you do not get enough color information or sufficient tonal range for the image during the scanning process, you will be stuck with a limited amount of information with which to work.

> ⚙ **Tonal Adjustments during Scanning** An interactive tutorial that explains and demonstrates why tonal optimization is necessary during scanning.

Figure 1 shows some examples of scanned images without optimizing the tonal range during the scan. Figure 1d shows a comparative scan of the same picture with the tonal range maximized *during* scanning.

The image scanned with a narrow tonal range (Figure 1a) looks dull and low in contrast. Although its tonal range may be adjusted later in an image editing program by stretching its histogram (Figure 1b), the result will not be as good as capturing the optimal tonal range during scanning.

A histogram is a graph showing the relative number of pixels at each color intensity level. Histogram-stretching concepts and techniques are discussed later in this chapter.

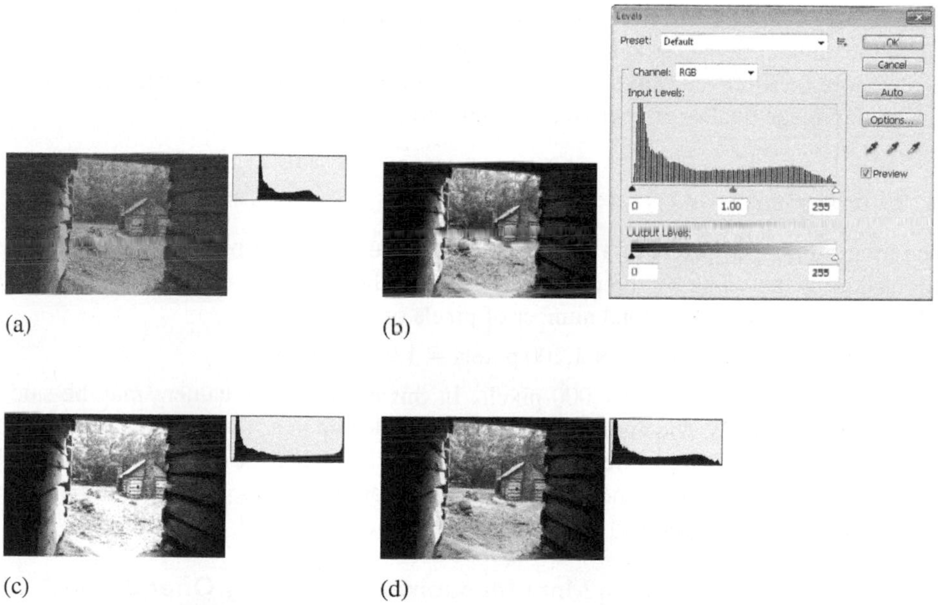

(a)

(b)

(c)

(d)

Screenshots from Adobe® Photoshop®. Copyright ©2011 by Adobe Systems, Inc. Reprinted with permission.

Figure 1 Scanned images with their histograms: (a) Scanned using a narrow tonal range. (b) The tonal range of the scanned image (a) is adjusted by stretching the histogram. (c) Scanned with highlights cropped off. (d) Scanned with a maximized tonal range. This image can be found on the insert.

---

[*]**Answer:** $\dfrac{1,300 \text{ pixels}}{150 \text{ ppi}} \approx 8.7 \text{ inches}$ $\dfrac{1,950 \text{ pixels}}{150 \text{ ppi}} = 13 \text{ inches}$

Figure 1c shows a scanned image with the highlights (i.e., the brightness) clipped off. The pixels whose highlight information is clipped off may contain subtle differences making up the details in the original image. However, they now all become white in the scanned image. Those highlights that have been cropped off during scanning cannot be recovered by *tonal adjustments* later in an image editing program.

4 CAPTURING DIGITAL IMAGES BY DIGITAL PHOTOGRAPHY

In traditional film photography, the image on a negative is made up of microscopic silver grains. The larger the negative, the more information about the scene is imprinted on the negative, and therefore the more information can be printed on paper. A larger negative takes less magnification to make a big print than a smaller one. This means that for prints of the same size, you get a sharper print from a larger negative than from a smaller one.

Some may consider the storage media used in the digital camera as the "digital film."

Digital cameras, on the other hand, use light sensors as the digital equivalent of film. The light hits the sensor and triggers electrical signals based on the light intensity. Such electrical signals are then converted into digital data and stored on the camera's storing device. Nowadays, the sensor that a digital camera uses is either a *CCD* (charge-coupled device) or a *CMOS* (complementary metal-oxide semiconductor). The size of the sensor and the number of light-sensing sites determine the maximum resolution of the digital camera.

Digital cameras are often advertised by the number of megapixels. Generally, the higher the number of megapixels, the more expensive the camera. But what is the practical meaning of the number of megapixels aside from being an indicator of the cost? If you are going to pay more for more megapixels, you should know what impact the number of megapixels has on the image quality of your creative photography work.

4.1 Megapixels

The total number of pixels in a digital image can be calculated by multiplying the pixel dimension of the width by the pixel dimension of the height. For example, an image of $1,600 \times 1,200$ pixels has a total number of pixels of:

$$1,600 \times 1,200 \text{ pixels} = 1,920,000 \text{ pixels}$$

One *megapixel* equals 1,000,000 pixels. In this example, the camera may be said to have 1.92 megapixels. The number tends to be rounded up in advertisements, so this camera would be advertised as offering 2 megapixels. The higher the total number of pixels, the higher the resolution of the image. But how exactly does the total number of pixels (reported in megapixels or not) affect any properties of an image?

Does a Digital Camera with More Megapixels Necessarily Offer Better Image Quality?

With the same CCD size, having more megapixels means smaller sensor sites on the CCD. This in turn means that the sensor may be less sensitive to light and may have more noise in the image.

The resolution of the captured image corresponds to the amount of detail. An image can capture more details from the original scene at a higher resolution. However, higher resolution alone does not necessarily mean higher image quality. For film cameras, with all other conditions being equal, the image quality depends on the quality of the lens optics, the size and quality of the film, and the film grain size. Similarly, the image quality for digital cameras depends on the optics, the size and quality of the CCD, and the camera electronics. It also depends on the camera's image processing software—how it processes the electronic data captured from the CCD into an RGB value for each pixel of the resulting image.

Does a Digital Camera with a Higher Megapixel Rating Give Bigger Prints?

A pixel is a point sample; it does not possess any physical dimensions. The pixel dimensions of a digital image alone do not provide any information about physical dimensions. Recall the equation in the previous section on scanning:

$$\text{Print Dimensions (in inches)} = \frac{\text{Pixel Dimensions (in pixels)}}{\text{Print Resolution (in pixels per inch or ppi)}}$$

The print size of a digital image depends on both the total number of pixels and the print resolution in ppi. A higher megapixel rating only tells you that the image has larger pixel dimensions—only one of the two variables in the equation. *If* the ppi is kept the same, then, yes, the image with more pixels will be printed bigger in size.

PRINT SIZE PER MEGAPIXEL

"Megapixel" is one of those loaded terms in digital imaging. The number of megapixels has been used to label a feature of a digital camera. However, what exactly are the implications of the term "megapixel"? Many consumers are concerned more about the actual print size of an image rather than the number of pixels. Is it possible to correlate the print size with megapixels?

The calculation of print size based on megapixels requires a deeper understanding of how the number of megapixels is calculated. There are many ways to approach the answer. So, let's spend some time analyzing the question and finding an answer.

As discussed previously, the physical size of the printed digital image depends on both its pixel dimensions and the ppi setting. However, given a ppi setting, it is possible to estimate the print size per megapixel.

Complicating the relationship between print size and megapixels is the fact that megapixels represent an *area*—that is, the product of the width (in pixels) by the height (in pixels). If you want to know the print size in width-by-height terms, you need to know the pixel dimensions of both the width and the height. Just the number of megapixels does not give you this information, because the same area size can be made up with many possible combinations of width and height. For 1 megapixel, the dimensions can be 1,000 × 1,000 pixels, 500 × 2,000 pixels, or approximately 1,155 × 866 pixels, and so on. Therefore, to correlate the print size to megapixels, you should think in area (square inches) first.

Approach 1

You first make up a combination of width and height (in pixels) that will come to 1 megapixel—say, 1,000 × 1,000 pixels.

If printing at 150 ppi, then for both width and height you get:

$$\frac{1,000 \text{ pixels}}{150 \text{ ppi}} \approx 6.67 \text{ inches}$$

That means 6.67 inches × 6.67 inches, which is **approximately 45 square inches per megapixel**.

Approach 2

Find an actual example of the image size of a digital camera. For example, a Canon EOS 5D Mark II can produce images of 5,616 × 3,744 pixels, that is, approximately 21 megapixels.

Printing at 150 ppi, you get:

37.44 inches × 24.96 inches ≈ 934 square inches per 21 megapixels

that is still approximately 45 square inches per megapixel.

In the first approach, we assume the width and height are the same. However, in the second approach, we start from 5,616 × 3,744 pixels and still come to the same number of square inches per megapixel. As you see, no matter what combination of width and height you use—even if you use 500 × 2,000 pixels—you will still come up with **about 45 square inches per megapixel** *if the image is printed at the same 150 ppi*.

Most digital cameras produce digital images with the width-to-height ratio of 4:3, not 1:1. If you want to take the 45 square inches apart to get a sense of width and height in a print size of **4:3** instead of thinking in area, then you will get a print size of **about 7.6 inches × 5.7 inches**. (Well, roughly 8 inches × 6 inches if you round it up.)

If the image is in **3:2** ratio, then it will be **about 8.2 inches × 5.4 inches**. (Note that these numbers are based on printing at 150 ppi.)

Let's emphasize again that the number of megapixels is a *product* of the pixel dimensions of width and height. But the same number of megapixels can be made up of many possible combinations of width and height. As you see from the above examples, both 7.6 inches × 5.7 inches (4:3 ratio) and 8.2 inches × 5.4 inches (3:2 ratio) can be from a 1-megapixel image, depending on the image's width-to-height ratio. If you are looking for a digital camera that can produce images that can be printed 8.2 inches × 5.4 inches at 150 ppi, a 1-megapixel camera that shoots photos in 3:2 ratio will meet your requirement. However, a 1-megapixel camera that only can produce images in 4:3 ratio will not meet your requirement.

❓ Self-Test Exercises: Megapixels[*]

1. The calculations in the previous example are based on 150-ppi printing. What is the print size per megapixel if the image is printed at 300 ppi?

2. From the previous examples, we have about 7.6 inches × 5.7 inches of print size per megapixel for 150-ppi printing if the image is in a 4:3 ratio. What will the print size for 2 megapixels be with the same conditions? Does the calculation involve multiplying both the 7.6 inches and 5.7 inches by 2? Why or why not? If not, then how do you calculate the answer?

---

[*] Answers to Self-Test Exercises: Megapixels:

1. About 11.1 square inches per megapixels if printed at 300 ppi.
   Explanation: Repeat either of the approaches shown in the example for 150 ppi. Let's follow approach 1. 1,000 pixels/300 ppi = 3.33 inches for both width and height. Thus, the area = 3.33 inches × 3.33 inches = 11.1 square inches.

2. Not simply multiplying both dimensions by 2, but by the square root of 2.
   Explanation: For 150 ppi, we have 45 square inches per megapixel. Thus, for 2 megapixels, we have 90 square inches. 90 square inches translate to about 11 inches × 8.2 inches.

> ⌂ Worksheet: Making Sense out of Megapixels This worksheet guides you in looking up digital camera specifications and understanding how to calculate megapixels to suit your needs.

4.2 Digital Cameras

Like traditional film cameras, there are point-and-shoot, interchangeable-lens, and *digital single-lens reflex (D-SLR)* models for digital cameras. Mobile devices, such as cell phones, also have built-in cameras. Most of these digital cameras can shoot high definition videos in addition to still photos. Most D-SLR cameras support interchangeable lenses. There are also digital medium-format cameras, which

> ⌂ Photography: Understanding Shutter Speed, Aperture, and ISO This supplementary reading explains the meaning and determination of the shutter speed, aperture, and ISO.

use larger imaging sensor to deliver more pixels than those based on the 35 mm film frame. For example, at the time of writing, medium format D-SLR cameras, such as Hasselblad D-SLR cameras, shoot images in 40 to 60 megapixels. Nikon and Canon D-SLR cameras that are based on the 35 mm frame, shoot images in the range of 10 to 25 megapixels.

5 DIGITAL IMAGE EDITING

In digital photography, the common traditional darkroom techniques have been translated into digital imaging tools by means of computer graphic algorithms. These tools often employ the language of photography and darkroom techniques, such as dodging, burning, filtering, cropping, and unsharp mask. If you have experience in darkroom techniques, you already may be familiar with the tasks for which these tools are intended. Digital image editing programs offer common tools (such as tonal adjustment, color correction, and sharpening) that allow you to perform image retouching. Many programs also support layers that allow you to composite and blend images in more creative ways beyond basic retouching. Creating a good digital image—aesthetics and craftsmanship—however, still relies on traditional imaging basics, not just knowing the "how-to" of using the digital image editing program.

The general steps and tools for image retouching are explained as follows. Not all of the steps are necessary for all images. For example, dust and scratch clean-up is often needed for scanned photographs but is not necessary for digital photographs directly captured from a digital camera. Cropping and straightening often are not necessary for digital photographs. However, you still may want to straighten crooked pictures or selectively crop pictures to create a better composition.

Step 1 **Cropping and straightening the image.**
If you scan a picture, the picture may be placed tilted on the scanner glass. Even if the image is taken from a digital camera, the scene may appear tilted. Also, you may appear have included nonpicture areas in the scan. You can straighten and crop the scanned image in the image editing program. For example, in Photoshop, you can use the *Crop tool* on the tool palette to achieve the cropping and straightening in one step.

Step 2 **Repairing imperfections.**
Dirt and dust are common imperfections in images acquired by scanning. You will need to inspect for and remove dust, scratches, and blemishes resulting from the scanning process. One of the common tools for cleaning up these random small imperfections is a clone tool with which you can clone from one area of the image

Single-lens reflex (SLR): An SLR camera reflects the image optically onto the focusing screen or viewfinder by using the light coming through the lens. This means SLR cameras allow you to see the image area accurately from the viewfinder. However, many non-SLR digital cameras now have an LCD for previewing.

An interchangeable lens is a lens that can be detached from the camera body and replaced with a different one. Cameras with interchangeable lenses allow you to use a wide variety of lenses, from telephoto and wide-angle to close-up lenses.

to cover the blemish. This is a direct copying from one part of the image to the other. Therefore, the part that you are using as the source should have the same color and texture as the area of the blemish to cover. Adobe Photoshop also has a tool called the ***Healing Brush*** that can match the shading and texture of the source with the area to be repaired.

Step 3 **Adjusting the overall contrast or tonal range of the image.**

Many image editing programs let you control the tonal range of the image by adjusting the ***highlights, midtones, and shadows*** of the image's histogram. For example, in Photoshop, you can choose `Image > Adjustments > Levels....` and you can stretch the histogram in the Level dialog box (Figure 2). Figure 3a shows that the contrast of the resulting image is higher. As demonstrated in Figure 3b, the histogram now shows a full tonal range from white to black. But the relative differences in color values among these four colors are maintained after the adjustment.

Figure 2 (a) An image of medium contrast consisting of four different colors. Three of the colors have the same number of pixels. The other has three times the number of pixels. No white or black color is in this image. Note: The numeric labels in cyan are not part of the image but are to show you the relationship between the color in the image and its corresponding "bar" in the histogram. (b) The histogram of this image. (c) Stretching the histogram by moving the highlight and shadow sliders to the edges.

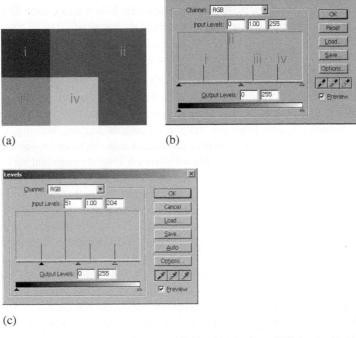

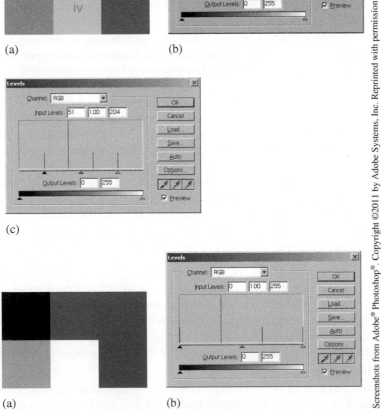

Figure 3 (a) The same 4-color image after stretching the histogram. (b) The histogram of this adjusted image.

Although there is a Brightness/Contrast command for image adjustments, stretching the histogram generally is the recommended tool over the simple brightness/contrast adjustment. This is because the relative color information of each pixel in the image remains the same when you stretch a histogram. However, the brightness/contrast adjustments will alter these relationships. (Compare Figure 4b to Figure 3b.)

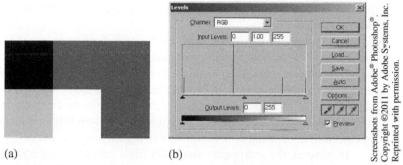

(a)   (b)

Figure 4 (a) The resulting 4-color image after adjustment using the Brightness/Contrast command. (b) The histogram of this adjusted image.

Step 4 **Removing color casts.**

An image sometimes contains *color casts*—the image appears tinted. Color casts may be introduced during scanning or may have existed in the original source picture. Many digital cameras have a built-in color-correction function. However, sometimes it may not color-correct the way you want, or there still may be a slight unwanted color cast due to a mix of different lighting conditions in the scene.

One way to offset the color cast is to adjust the *color balance*. To use this tool, you need to determine the imbalanced colors and then balance them by offsetting the color casts. In Photoshop, there are three sliders in the Color Balance dialog box (Figure 5), each labeled with a color at either end. The color pairs are complementary colors: cyan–red, magenta–green, and yellow–blue. For example, if your image has a red cast, you should drag the slider away from the red toward the cyan end to offset the red cast. The color correction can be selectively applied to the highlights, midtones, or shadows of the image. For example, darker areas often contain a blue cast while the brighter areas in the same image do not. In this case, you may want to target the shadow areas in removing the blue cast so that the color correction does not inadvertently add a yellow cast on the other areas of the image.

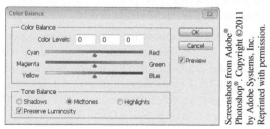

Figure 5 A Color Balance dialog box

Step 5 Fine-tuning specific parts of the image.

Note that the previous editing steps are applied to the whole image. However, certain parts of the image may need specific enhancements. You can select those parts using selection tools before applying the adjustment. There are also other tools for fine-tuning specific parts of the image without having to make a selection first. Tools such as the dodge tool to bring out highlights, the burn tool to bring out shadows, and the sponge tool to saturate or desaturate colors work like a paint brush (except that you paint to apply the adjustment instead of a color).

Step 6 Sharpening the image.

Scanned images usually look a little soft-focused. Scaling an image also can make the image soft-focused. Even if your image is a straight digital photograph from a digital camera, it is a good idea to experiment with sharpening at the end of the image retouching to see if it improves the image's overall clarity. In any case, you should wait to do the sharpening until the final step in the editing process. To understand why the sharpening step should be the last step in the retouching process, you need to understand how sharpening in digital imaging works.

In general, the sharpening algorithm finds edges by looking for pixels with significant color differences from their neighboring pixels. Sharpening creates the illusion of sharpness by lightening the pixels on the lighter side of the edge and darkening on the other side. Thus, applying sharpening will alter the colors in the image. Because the edges are detected by the extent of color differences, all the color and tonal corrections or adjustments have to be made prior to the sharpening. Otherwise, the edge detection would have been based on the incorrect colors.

Sharpening should be the very last step of your image editing project. One exception is when you need to add elements with crisp, clean edges, such as a border, to the image; in this case you should do so after the sharpening. If you apply sharpening to a solid-color border, the edge of the border may not remain clean and sharp in the final image.

The sharpening tool in Photoshop is under `Filter > Sharpen`. There are four sharpening tools under Sharpen: `Sharpen`, `Sharpen Edges`, `Sharpen More`, and `Unsharp Mask....`

Generally, the ***Unsharp Mask tool*** is the recommended sharpening tool because it gives you more control on the sharpening settings. Using `Unsharp Mask...`, you can specify these options:

- `Amount`: the amount of the contrast increase around the edges
- `Radius`: the radius of the surrounding area where the color comparison and the sharpening take place
- `Threshold`: how much the pixels differ from surrounding pixels in order to be identified as "edges" to be sharpened

There are no magic numbers for these settings. It depends on the resolution of the image. For high-resolution images, experiment with an `Amount` setting between 100% and 200%, a `Radius` setting between 1 and 3, and a `Threshold` between 0 and 10. Lower these numbers for low-resolution images. For low-resolution images, an `Amount` between 50% and 100%, a `Radius` between 1 and 2, and a `Threshold` between 0 and 2 would be a good starting point for you to experiment with. Be careful not to oversharpen an image. If you notice increased graininess or unnatural halos around edges, you have probably oversharpened the image. Setting the `Amount` too high will exaggerate the intensity of the lighter and darker lines around edges, creating unnatural halos around edges. The halos will be spread out and become even more noticeable if the `Radius` setting is too high. If you notice increased graininess, you will need to increase the `Threshold` setting.

If you want to limit the sharpening to the more pronounced edges, raise the threshold value. The softer edges will be left unsharpened. The graininess resulting from sharpening is especially an undesired side effect for skin texture. Thus, raising the threshold can be an effective way in sharpening portraits—sharpen the image while leaving the soft skin texture soft. What would be the best threshold setting for portraits, then? It depends on your image—its content and resolution. But a threshold setting between 3 and 10 would be a good starting point for you to experiment with.

THE ORDER OF THE IMAGE RETOUCHING STEPS

When retouching an image, try to keep the order of the image retouching steps listed in this section. Performing these steps out of order or jumping back and forth among steps may cause unwanted effects on the image. To understand why the order is important, let's think about the following questions.

Questions[†]

1. What happens if you sharpen an image *before* stretching the histogram or performing color correction?
2. What happens if you stretch the histogram or perform color correction *before* cropping off the unwanted areas from an image?
3. What happens if you apply dodging and burning *before* removing the color casts?

Image Retouching (Lab) Use the example image available from the text's Web site and practice the retouching steps discussed.

The word "unsharp" in the unsharp mask sounds counterintuitive to the sharpening function of the tool. However, the unsharp mask is a traditional film technique for sharpening an image by using a slightly out-of-focus (thus unsharp) duplicate negative as a mask. The original negative is sandwiched with this duplicate (an unsharp mask) during printing. This will make the lighter side of the edges lighter and the darker side of the edges darker, thereby making the image look sharper. Heightening the contrast between the lighter and darker lines around edges is basically the same technique of unsharp mask in digital imaging used to create a sharper look in an image.

[†] Answers to Questions:

1. The sharpening process involves detecting edges based on color differences of neighboring pixels. If sharpening is applied before the tonal and color corrections, the edge detection will be based on incorrect color information. In addition, sharpening increases the contrast of the edges. This contrast increase may exaggerate the problems (such as color casts) before they are fixed.
2. If you stretch the histogram or perform color correction before the cropping, you will be including a lot of unwanted color that should not be taken into consideration.
3. Color casts usually appear evenly in an image. However, the color cast at the dodged or burnt areas will be exaggerated or lessen. Either way, the color cast becomes uneven throughout the image. This will make it difficult to remove the color cast simply by applying one setting of color balance.

6 COLOR AND TONAL ADJUSTMENTS

There are a variety of color and tonal adjustment tools available in image editing programs. Depending on the program, the options available for the tools and the interface may vary. However, generally the tools work by mapping the existing color or tonal values of the pixels to new ones. The common tools include adjusting the histogram, color balance, color curves, and hue/saturation. Different tools use different graphical representations to map color or tonal values of the pixels in the image and thus offer different types of control. Adjusting the histogram (Section 6.1) lets you define and map the shadows, midtones, and highlights using sliders. The ***Color Balance tool*** lets you offset one color by moving the corresponding slider toward its complementary color. This is useful for removing color casts of images. This tool is discussed in the previous section on digital image retouching to remove color casts. The ***Curve tool*** (Section 6.3) lets you remap the color and tonal range by altering the shape of a curve. The horizontal axis of the graph used in the Curve tool represents the original color values of the pixels (input levels). Its vertical axis represents the new color values after adjustment (output levels). The ***Hue/Saturation tool*** has three basic controls—hue, saturation, and lightness.

6.1 Understanding and Reading Histograms

Parts of Sections 6.1 and 6.2 are available as a standalone online interactive tutorial at the text's Web site. You can read through the text while experimenting interactively in the tutorial. There are two practice exercise sections at the end of the tutorial to test your knowledge of applying histograms to image editing.

A ***histogram*** of an image is a bar chart that shows the relative number of pixels plotted against the color value. Figure 6 shows an example of a grayscale image and its histogram. In this example, the *x*-axis of the histogram is the gray level (with the darkest value on the left), and the *y*-axis is the relative number of pixels in the image that have the corresponding shade of gray. The histogram in Figure 6b does not look like the kind of bar chart you may have seen in business presentations. This is because this picture has a full range of 256 gray levels and the bars are packed next to each other, making the histogram look like a mountain range rather than a statistical bar chart.

(a)   (b)

Yue-Ling Wong

Figure 6 (a) A grayscale image. (b) The histogram of the image.

To learn how to read a histogram, let's first look at a very simple image that has only five different gray colors. The image shown in Figure 7a has five main different gray colors. Each gray takes up a different amount of space in the image. The background color is the lightest gray in this image. It is represented by the rightmost line (line [v]) in the histogram (Figure 7b). Notice that it is also the longest line in the histogram because this background color occupies the largest area in the image. In fact, the line is so long compared to other lines that it is truncated.

? Self-Test Exercises: Reading Histograms[‡]

1. Which gray has the least number of pixels; that is which solid gray area is the smallest?

2. For each of the bars, or lines, in the histogram in Figure 6, identify and label its corresponding gray color in the image, by comparing their relative gray levels.

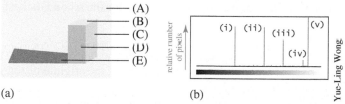

(a)   (b)

Figure 7 (a) A simple grayscale image. (b) The histogram for the image.

6.2 Applying Histograms to Adjustment of Brightness and Contrast

Many image editing programs let you adjust image *brightness* and *contrast* with the image's histogram. For example, the histogram tool can be found in `Image > Adjustments > Levels...` in Adobe Photoshop. When you choose to adjust levels, a dialog box will appear showing the histogram of the image (Figure 8). There are three sliders on the *x*-axis of the histogram:

- A black slider on the left end marks the darkest color (shadow).
- A white slider on the right end marks the brightest color (highlight).
- A gray slider in the middle marks the 50% intensity of the color (midtone).

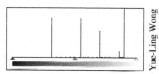

Figure 8 A histogram showing three sliders: black (shadow), gray (midtone), and white (highlight)

You can move these triangles to modify the image's *brightness* and *contrast*. You can map the pixels to the darkest by repositioning the black slider. For example, if you drag the black slider to the peak that corresponds to the second darkest gray color (Figure 9b), you set this gray color as the darkest color (i.e., black) in the image. Any color that is originally darker than this gray will become black after this adjustment of the black slider. In the original image (Figure 7a), the front of the block and the block's shadow were in different tones

---

[‡] Answers to the Self-Test Exercises:

1. (B)

2. (A)–(v), (B)–(iv), (C)–(iii), (D)–(ii), (E)–(i)

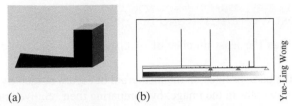

(a)   (b)

Figure 9 (a) The resulting grayscale image after moving the black slider toward the right. (b) The black slider is moved to where the bar for the second darkest color of the image is.

of gray. But after the adjustment, they become black and indistinguishable (Figure 9a). As you see, if you move the black slider past the left end of the original histogram, details that were once made up of this area of gray will be lost.

The position of the white slider defines the brightness color—white. Similar to the black slider, if you move the white slider to the left, past the right end of the original histogram, the highlights that were once in this area of gray will be lost because they will all become white.

HISTOGRAM

Activity/Exercise

Experiment by dragging the sliders and observe how the position of the sliders affects the brightness and contrast in the image in the interactive tutorial or in Photoshop.

- Drag the white slider to the second peak on the right in the histogram. Note which colors in the image turn white.
- Drag the white slider to the rightmost peak and the black slider to the leftmost peak in the histogram. Note how the contrast of the image changes.

By defining the new positions of the black and the white sliders, you remap the whole spectrum of color values of the pixels. By repositioning the black slider to the leftmost peak and the white slider to the rightmost peak, you *stretch* the histogram (Figure 10a). That means you make the darkest color in the image to be black, and the brightest color in the

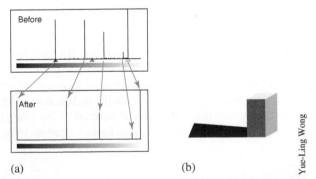

(a)   (b)

Figure 10 (a) The histograms before and after stretching. (b) The resulting image after stretching the histogram.

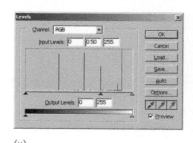
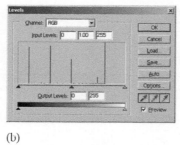
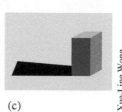

(a)   (b)   (c)

Yue-Ling Wong

Figure 11 (a) The original histogram of Figure 7 with the midtone slider moved to the higher value (brighter side). (b) The histogram of the resulting image after the adjustment. (c) The resulting image after the adjustment.

image to be white, as in Figure 10b. All other colors will be mapped in between relative to each other. By stretching the histogram, you maximize the use of the full spectrum of the gray tones. The overall contrast of the image is increased because the color value differences between colors are increased.

You also can move the gray slider in the middle to set the midtone. For example, if you move the gray slider to a new position, as shown in Figure 11a, you set the gray color that is originally a lighter gray as the midtone (value of 128 for an 8-bit color). If you click OK to accept the change and then look at the histogram again, you will see the bar that the gray slider was repositioned to is now in the middle (Figure 11b). That is, the color is changed to the middle gray. All other colors are remapped accordingly. As a result, any color darker than this is mapped to between 0 and 128. Any color brighter than this is mapped to between 128 and 255.

Because you shift the midtone to the lighter gray of the original image, the resulting image becomes darker overall.

However, if you shift the midtone to the gray color that is originally a darker gray (Figure 12a), the resulting image becomes lighter overall (Figure 12c). If you look at the histogram of the resulting image, you will see the bar that the gray slider was repositioned to is now in the middle (Figure 12b). That is, the color is changed to the middle gray. Again, all other colors are remapped accordingly.

In Figure 12, no color is darker than the midtone. Thus, all the bars in the histogram are positioned on the right half of the histogram. The image appears washed out.

In summary, a histogram is a bar chart showing the relative number of pixels versus color values. The color values of the *x*-axis are usually from 0 to 255. For a grayscale image (like the example shown here), the *x*-axis has 256 levels of possible gray tones, from 0 to 255—with 0 being black and 255 being white. The middle gray has a value of 128. For a color image, you can choose to adjust the levels for each of the red, green, and blue channels. You also can choose to adjust all three channels together.

To illustrate the concept of histograms, the examples here adjusted the levels by moving the three triangular sliders one at a time in the histogram. However, imaging editing programs, such as Adobe Photoshop, let you adjust the shadows, highlights, and midtones simultaneously by directly entering their values or moving the sliders.

It is not only in image editing programs that you encounter histograms; many digital cameras and scanners show you

> **Light Metering Emulation of Photography**
> This emulates photographing a still life and illustrates the relationship between spot-metering and the resulting image's midtone.

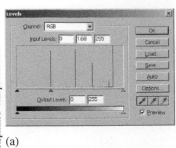

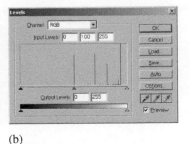

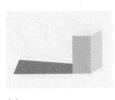

(a) (b) (c)

Figure 12 (a) The histogram of Figure 7 with the midtone slider moved to the lower value (darker side). (b) The histogram of the resulting image after the adjustment. (c) The resulting image after the adjustment.

In Photoshop, you can add a new selection to the existing selection by holding down the Shift key while selecting. Hold down the ALT (Windows) or Option (Mac OS) key for subtracting.

the histogram of the captured image. This helps you see if you are getting the optimal tonal range of the captured image right away. Being able to see the histogram instantaneously helps you decide immediately if you need to take the photograph again while you are on location.

> **Understanding and Applying Histograms** There are two parts of this learning aid: an interactive tutorial and practice exercises. The tutorial explains how to interpret an image's histogram and make tonal adjustments using histograms.
>
> To test your knowledge of histograms, check out the two interactive exercises in the tutorial:
>
> **Exercise I: Reading Histograms.** Practice relating the appearance of a histogram to the image characteristics.
>
> **Exercise II: Improving Image Contrast and Brightness.** Identify the problem of the image by examining the histogram, and then improve it.

6.3 Curves Adjustment Tool

Curve adjustment tool lets you remap the color and tonal range by using the shape of a 2-D curve.

In a 2-D plot, there are two axes: x-axis (horizontal) and the y-axis (vertical). The line or the curve shows the relationship between the x- and y-values. For adjustment curves, both the x- and y-axes represent the spectrum of the tonal values from darkest to brightest. Conceptually, each axis is similar to the horizontal axis in a histogram—except that now you have both the vertical and horizontal axes representing the tonal range shown as a gradient bar next to each axis.

So, how are the x- and y-axes different? In Photoshop, by default, the x-axis represents the input values and the y-axis the output values. Think of the input as "before" and the output as "after"—as in before and after applying the adjustment using the Curve tool.

Above or Below the Diagonal Line—Darker or Lighter

The default diagonal straight line shown in Figure 13 does not alter the tonal value of the image. For example, the color arrow in Figure 13 shows that a light gray on the x-axis (input) is mapped to the exact same light gray on the y-axis (output).

A curve that is shown in Figure 14 lowers the tonal value of the original image (i.e., the image becomes darker). For example, the color arrow in Figure 14 shows that a light gray on the x-axis (input) is mapped to a dark gray on the y-axis (output).

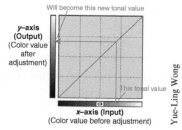

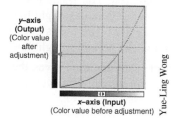

Figure 13 A diagonal straight line in the Curves adjustment tool.

Figure 14 This curve specifies lowering the original tonal value.

To help you see whether the resulting tonal value will be darker or brighter, you can imagine the presence of the default diagonal straight line—a straight line drawn from the upper-right corner to the lower-left corner—like the colored diagonal line shown in Figure 15.

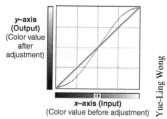

Figure 15 Imagine a diagonal straight line, like the colored line shown here.

- If the portion of the curve is above the default straight line, then the resulting color will be brighter than that before the adjustment.
- If below, then the resulting color will be darker.

Because the direction of lightness on the axes can be reversed, be careful which direction you are using. No matter which direction is used it will give the same result if you adjust the curve correctly. Let's look at an example shown in Figure 16.

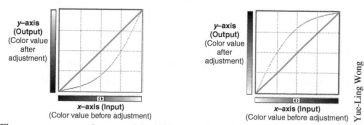

Figure 16 The same curve shown with different directions of the *x*- and *y*-axis (a) Axes with default direction from black to white. (b) Axes with a reversed direction from white to black.

- Figure 16a: The *y*-axis goes from dark to light upward. The portion of the curve is below the default straight line. The resulting color will be darker.
- Figure 16b: The *y*-axis goes from light to dark upward. The portion of the curve is above the default straight line. The resulting color will be darker, as in Figure 16a.

Either representation gives the same result—in this example, the tone of the image will become darker. The cyan-colored line is included to help you visualize the diagonal line.

Curve Steepness and Image Contrast

The curvature of the curve controls the contrast. If a region of a curve is steeper than the default straight line, then the contrast of the tonal range within that region will be increased. In the example shown in Figure 16, the contrast of the highlight areas is increased, but the contrast of the shadow areas is lowered.

In summary, two properties of the Curves adjustment tool that determine the color adjustment are

- Being above or below the diagonal line determines the brighter or darker adjustment
- The steepness of the curve controls the contrast.

🖱 **Understanding and Applying Curves for Color Adjustments** An interactive tutorial and exercises help you understand the Curves tool for image adjustment.

❓ Self-Test Exercises: Interpreting Curves**

I.

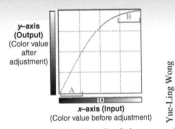

Figure 17 An adjustment curve for Part I of the exercise.

The following questions are based on the adjustment curve shown in Figure 17.

1. After the adjustment, the image will be _____.
   - A. brighter
   - B. darker

2. _____ of the curve is steeper than the default diagonal line, and thus after the adjustment, the contrast for the tonal range within that region will be _____.
   - A. Region A; higher
   - B. Region A; lower
   - C. Region B; higher
   - D. Region B; lower

II. The "S-curve"

The "S-curve" often is used to boost the overall contrast of an image. Let's see why.

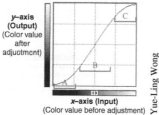

Figure 18 An adjustment curve for Part II of the exercise.

The following questions are based on the adjustment curve shown in Figure 18.

1. After the adjustment, the **highlights** (Region C) will become _____.
    A. brighter
    B. darker

2. After the adjustment, the **shadows** (Region A) will become _____.
    A. brighter
    B. darker

3. The curve in _____ is steeper than the default diagonal line, and thus after the adjustment, the contrast for the tonal range in that region will become _____.
    A. Region A; higher   D. Region B; lower
    B. Region A; lower   E. Region C; higher
    C. Region B; higher   F. Region C; lower

III.

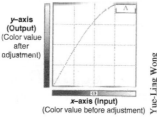

Figure 19 An adjustment curve for Part III of the exercise.

The following questions are based on the adjustment curve shown in Figure 19.

1. After the adjustment, the **highlights** (Region A) will become _____.
    A. all white
    B. all black

2. After the adjustment, the tonal values outside of Region A, will become _____.
    A. higher (brighter)
    B. lower (darker)

3. The curve other than in Region A is _____ than the diagonal line, and thus after the adjustment, the contrast for the tonal range outside of Region A will be _____.

    A. steeper; higher
    B. steeper; lower
    C. less steep; higher
    D. less steep, lower

IV.

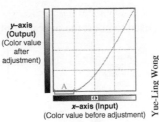

Figure 20 An adjustment curve for Part IV of the exercise.

The following questions are based on the adjustment curve shown in Figure 20.
1. After the adjustment, the **shadows** (Region A) will become _____.
   A. all white
   B. all black
2. After the adjustment, the tonal values outside of Region A will become _____.
   A. higher (brighter)
   B. lower (darker)
3. The curve other than in Region A is _____ than the diagonal line, and thus after the adjustment, the contrast for the tonal range outside of Region A will be

   _____.

  A. steeper; higher   C. less steep; higher
  B. steeper; lower   D. less steep; lower

V.

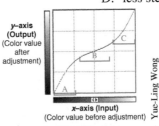

Figure 21 An adjustment curve for Part V of the exercise.

The following questions are based on the adjustment curve shown in Figure 21.
1. After the adjustment, the **highlights** (Region C) will be _____.
   A. brighter
   B. darker
2. After the adjustment, the **shadows** (Region A) will be _____.
   A. brighter
   B. darker
3. The curve in _____ is **less steep** than the default diagonal line, and thus after the adjustment, the contrast for the tonal range in that region will be _____.
   A. Region A; higher
   B. Region A; lower
   C. Region B; higher
   D. Region B; lower
   E. Region C; higher
   F. Region C; lower

4. After the adjustment, the **contrast** of the **highlights** (Region C) will be _____.
   A. higher
   B. lower

5. After the adjustment, the **contrast** of the **midtones** (Region B) will be _____.
   A. higher
   B. lower

6. After the adjustment, the **contrast** of the **shadows** (Region **A**) will be _____.
   A. higher
   B. lower

7 SELECTION TOOLS IN IMAGE EDITING PROGRAMS

The ability to select a specific region of an image is crucial in image editing. Often, it is necessary to fine-tune specific parts of the image. If you apply any tonal or color changes on a selection, the changes are confined to the selected area; the rest of the image is protected from the alteration. Being able to make a specific selection is also important in compositing or collaging images together because once a selection is made, you can extract the selected parts of the image.

There are a variety of selection tools available in image editing programs. However, instead of trying to list and explain these tools one by one, we will categorize these tools in terms of their specialties or the way they are designed to work:

- **Predefined shapes:** The *Marquee tools* provide predefined shapes, such as rectangular and elliptical.
- **Lasso:** The *Lasso tool* and *Polygonal tool* let you create an irregularly shaped selection. The *Magnetic Lasso tool* makes a selection by tracing edges and thus is useful for selecting an area that has well-defined edges.
- **By color:** With the *Magic Wand tool*, you can specify the tolerance or the similarity of the color in the surrounding pixels to be included in the selection. You also can use the *Eyedropper tool* to pick out a color in the foreground color chip, and then choose Select > Color Range....
- **By painting with a brush to select or deselect a specific area:** Editing in *Quick Mask mode* allows you to use the paintbrush to paint in black to deselect, white to select, and grays to create semitransparent selections, as well as feathering and anti-aliasing.
- **By drawing an outline around the area to be selected:** The *Pen tool* lets you draw a vector shape outline around an area that you want to select.

** Answers to the self-test exercises:

  I. (1) **A**; (2) **A**
 II. (1) **A**; (2) **B**; (3) **C**
III. (1) **A**; (2) **A**; (3) **A**
IV. (1) **B**; (2) **B**; (3) **A**
 V. (1) **B**; (2) **A**; (3) **D**; (4) **A**; (5) **B**; (6) **A**

If you move the selection by using any of the selection tools instead of the Move tool, you will move the floating selection only. This may be useful if you want to use the shape of that selection for another area in the image.

To create a complex selection, you often need to use multiple selection tools to add, subtract, or intersect selections. After you have made a selection, you can manipulate the selected pixels. You can use the **Move tool** to move the pixels in the selected area. You can soften the hard edges of the selection by applying feathering (in Photoshop, choose `Select > Refine Edge...`). You also can save the selection (`Select > Save Selection...`) and load the selection (`Select > Load Selection...`) later. This is particularly useful if the selection you have made is time consuming and complex. It is a good idea to save the selection after each step in case you accidentally lose the selection, and, of course, save the final selection so you can load the selection at any time later.

> ✏ Photoshop Basics: Selection A screen-capture movie gives a quick demonstration of some of the selection tools in Photoshop. A worksheet exercise is also available.

> 🖰 Image Alteration (Lab) Use the example images (available from the text's Web site) to practice selectively altering areas.

8 LAYER BASICS AND ADVANCED LAYER TECHNIQUES

Layers in Photoshop are like a stack of transparencies; the content in a layer can block out those in the layers beneath it. However, layers are more than that, because you can also set the opacity and blending mode of each layer. You can rearrange the stacking order by dragging a layer in the **Layers panel** up or down the stack. Many image editing programs support layers. The following discussion is based on Adobe Photoshop but should be applicable to other image editing programs that support those features discussed here.

In Photoshop, there is a special layer called Background that is listed in italics in the Layers panel. This **Background layer** always stays at the bottom of the stack and cannot be rearranged. In addition, it is not a transparent layer. When you use the **Eraser tool** to erase the image content on this layer, you replace the content with the color that is set in the background color chip. However, erasing the image content on a regular layer will reveal transparency. The Background layer can be converted to a regular standard layer, for example, by double-clicking on it in the Layers palette.

> ✏ Photoshop Basics: Using Layers A screen-capture movie gives a quick demonstration of commonly used features of the Layers panel in Photoshop. A worksheet exercise is also available.

You can create new layers, delete layers, rename layers, control the visibility of each layer, and copy layers from one file to another. You also can apply a layer style (`Layer > Layer Style`), such as a drop shadow or bevel, to a layer. You can select multiple layers or link them together, so that you can move or scale them simultaneously.

Adjustment layers are used for applying image adjustments, such as levels and color balance, to a layer without altering the pixel content of that layer. An adjustment layer is a separate layer by itself. Think of it as a pair of sunglasses through which you see a world with reduced UV light intensity and glare but the sunglasses do not actually change the lighting condition of the world. Because the adjustment layer does not alter pixel content of other layers, the advantage of using an adjustment layer instead of directly applying the adjustment on an individual layer is that you can change the adjustment settings any time. In addition, to remove the adjustment any time, you can simply delete the adjustment layer. You can also hide the adjustment effect temporarily by turning off its layer visibility just like any other layers. An adjustment layer applies the adjustment to all the layers below it but you can apply the adjustment to specific layers by grouping them with the adjustment layer and changing the blending mode of the group from Pass Through to Normal.

A *layer mask* associated with a layer lets you *obscure*—just block, not delete—part of the image on that layer. This nondestructive method of editing offers the advantage of preserving the original image. Later, if you change your mind in how you want the image on that layer to show, you can edit the mask or remove the whole mask. See Figure 22 for an example of a layer mask. The black color of the mask hides the image while the white lets the content of the image show through. Figure 23a shows how the resulting image of the example shown in Figure 22 may look.

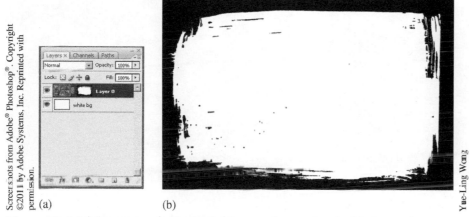

(a)   (b)

Yue-Ling Wong

Figure 22 (a) A layers panel showing a layer mask associated with the top layer. (b) The layer mask.

The *clipping mask* works very similarly to the layer mask (Figure 23). Whereas a layer mask is associated with one layer and only masks that one layer, the clipping mask works like a cookie cutter by cutting through multiple layers that are in the same group. In this example the clipping group is made up of two layers—the base layer (Figure 23c) that acts as a mask for the entire group, and a layer with the image (Figure 23d).

> ✎ **Making Composites: Example 1—Replicating an Object in Its Environment** In this example, the final image (Figure 24b) contains an extra object—a humanoid chain sculpture—which is not in the original image (Figure 24a). This example demonstrates the following aspects of image editing:
>
> • Application of selection
> • Scaling with the perspective in mind
> • Creation of shadows

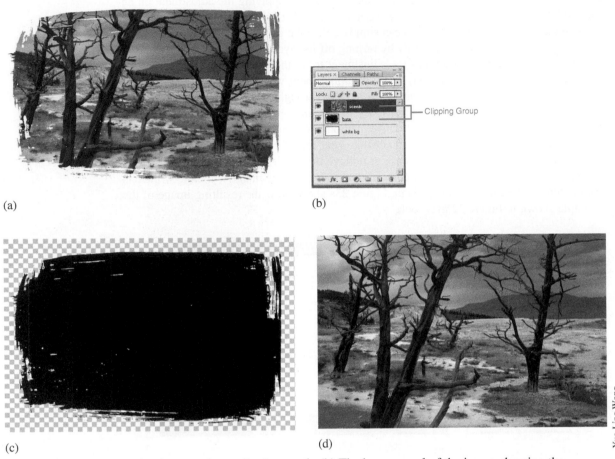

(a)

(b) Clipping Group

(c)

(d)

Yue-Ling Wong

Figure 23 (a) The resulting image using a clipping mask. (b) The layers panel of the image showing the arrangement of the layers. (c) The base layer of the clipping mask. (d) The image in the non-base layer of the clipping mask.

(a)

(b)

Yue-Ling Wong

Figure 24 (a) The original digital photograph. (b) The final composite.

> ✐ **Making Composites: Example 2—Recreating a Sky Background** In this example, the final image (Figure 25c) contains an artificial sky and is created by compositing two digital images (Figures 25a and b). The tools used to make the composite include:
>
> - Layer blending mode
> - Layer mask
> - Layer style
> - Filters
> - Stamp tool
> - Dodge tool

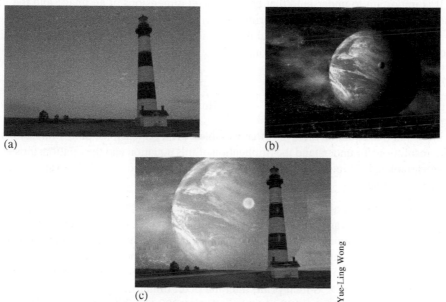

(a)　　　　　　　　　　　(b)

(c)

Yue-Ling Wong

Figure 25 (a) The original digital photograph. (b) An image that is used as an artificial sky background. (c) The final composite.

9 PRINTING THE FINAL IMAGE

In real-life situations, if you want to change the size of an object, you would think of scaling it up or down physically. However, the intuitive sense of size that you have learned from the physical world is not always applicable to the concept of size in digital images. The size of a digital image is described in terms of pixel dimensions. The physical print size (in inches) of an image depends on its pixel dimensions and the print resolution (in pixels per inch or ppi). The same image can be printed at different physical sizes using different ppi settings. Image editing programs let you resize or scale images by changing the pixel dimensions of the image. There are also options for changing the physical print size (in inches). The print size can be changed with or without changing the pixel dimensions.

To preserve the detail and quality of an image, it is best not to scale the original pixel dimensions of the image. The reason is as follows. As you have learned from the discussion of sampling and quantizing in digital images, the amount of detail in an image is related to its original pixel dimensions, which, in turn, are determined by the sampling rate. When you increase the pixel dimensions of an image by resizing, new pixels are added. But the color information of these new pixels is generated by interpolating the color information of the existing pixels. Therefore, although the pixel dimensions of the image increase, such resizing does not really add new detail to the image because it is only interpolating the existing pixel information. In fact, the resulting image often appears blurry. When you shrink an image by reducing its pixel dimensions, some pixels have to be removed; that is, you lose information. In addition, the color information of the remaining pixels is altered to fit the new size.

It is important to understand that both the pixel dimensions of an image and the image resolution (ppi) affect the image's print size. This relationship is discussed in the section on megapixels. It applies to all digital images, not only images that are obtained by digital photography. Let's revisit the equation.

$$\text{Print Dimension (in inches)} = \frac{\text{Pixel Dimension (in pixels)}}{\text{Print Resolution (in pixels per inch or ppi)}}$$

Note that this equation involves three variables: print dimensions, pixel dimensions, and print resolution. To understand the implication of this equation and the relationships among these variables, let's look at three different scenarios in each of which one variable is fixed at a known value.

Scenario 1 **Maintaining the Physical Print Dimensions**

If you want to print an image at higher print resolution (ppi) but maintain the print dimensions, you will need to increase the image's pixel dimensions. For example, an image of 600 × 600 pixels printed at 100 ppi will give a print of 6 inches × 6 inches. If you want to print at 200 ppi and still have a 6-inch × 6-inch print, then the pixel dimensions of the image need to be increased from 600 × 600 pixels to 1,200 × 1,200 pixels.

$$\text{Print Dimension (in inches)} = \frac{\text{Pixel Dimension (in pixels)}}{\text{Print Resolution (in pixels per inch or ppi)}}$$

$$\frac{600 \text{ pixels}}{100 \text{ ppi}} = \textbf{6 inches}$$

$$\frac{1,200 \text{ pixels}}{200 \text{ ppi}} = \textbf{6 inches}$$

$$\frac{1,800 \text{ pixels}}{300 \text{ ppi}} = \textbf{6 inches}$$

and so forth.

Scenario 2 **Maintaining the Pixel Dimensions**

If you want to print an image at higher physical print dimensions but do not want to scale up the image's pixel dimensions, you will need to lower print resolution (ppi). Using the previous example, an image of 600 × 600 pixels printed at 100 ppi will give a print of 6 inches × 6 inches.

$$\text{Print Dimension (in inches)} = \frac{\text{Pixel Dimension (in pixels)}}{\text{Print Resolution (in pixels per inch or ppi)}}$$

$$\frac{\textbf{600 pixels}}{100 \text{ ppi}} = 6 \text{ inches}$$

$$\frac{\textbf{600 pixels}}{200 \text{ ppi}} = 3 \text{ inches}$$

$$\frac{\textbf{600 pixels}}{300 \text{ ppi}} = 2 \text{ inches}$$

and so forth.

Scenario 3 **Maintaining the Print Resolution (ppi)**

Given a fixed ppi, an image with higher pixel dimensions will give a larger printout. Using the previous example, you see how the print size changes with the image's pixel dimension:

$$\text{Print Dimension (in inches)} = \frac{\text{Pixel Dimension (in pixels)}}{\text{Print Resolution (in pixels per inch or ppi)}}$$

$$\frac{600 \text{ pixels}}{\textbf{100 ppi}} = 6 \text{ inches}$$

$$\frac{1{,}200 \text{ pixels}}{\textbf{100 ppi}} = 12 \text{ inches}$$

$$\frac{1{,}800 \text{ pixels}}{\textbf{100 ppi}} = 18 \text{ inches}$$

and so forth.

So, how are these scenarios translated into the settings used in an image editing program? To adjust the output resolution or print size of an image, look in the image size setting. In Photoshop, for example, it can be found under `Image > Image Size....`

The setting of the `Resample Image` option (Figure 26) separates Scenario 2 from the other two scenarios. For Scenario 2, in order to maintain the pixel dimensions of the image, you will need to uncheck the Resample Image option (Figure 26a). Then, when you alter the width and height in the Document Size section, the print resolution (ppi) will be updated automatically, and vice versa, if you change the print resolution.

If you check the Resample Image option (Figure 26b), then both Scenarios 1 and 3 apply. With the Resample Image option on, the pixel dimensions are allowed to vary. That is, the pixel dimensions can be varied with the print resolution (ppi) while maintaining the print size. They also can be varied with the print size while maintaining the print resolution (ppi).

Printer resolution is measured in dots per inch (dpi)—the number of ink dots per inch. Color inkjet printers produce a microscopic spray of ink that appears to be very tiny dots of ink. The number of color inks that a printer uses determines the number of colors of these ink dots. Although a printer uses only a limited number of color inks, these tiny ink dots are very close to each other and, by varying the relative number of different color dots on paper, can produce the many different colors by optical mixing. The color of a single pixel of an image is represented

Turning the Resample Image option on means that scaling of the image is allowed. Scaling the pixel dimensions of an image is referred to as resampling because the number of samples (pixels) is changed.

🖰 Optical Color Mixing in Pointillism, Dithering, and Inkjet Printing An interactive demonstration of optical color mixing.

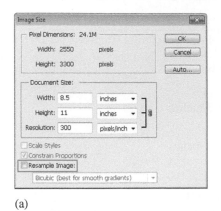
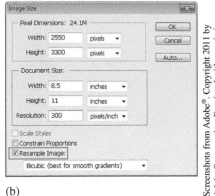

(a)   (b)

Figure 26 Adobe Photoshop's Image Size dialog box. (a) Uncheck the Resample Image option to change the Document Size settings while maintaining the pixel dimensions (Scenario 2). (b) Check the Resample Image option to allow scaling of pixel dimensions to maintain the print dimensions (Scenario 1) or print resolution (Scenario 3).

⏚ Worksheet: Image ppi versus Printer dpi Learn the difference between the printer dpi and image ppi by:

1. Experimenting with how the image ppi affects the output dimensions of the image.
2. Experimenting with how the printer dpi affects the printing quality of the image.

by a group of these printer dots. Do not confuse the image print resolution (ppi) with the printer resolution (dpi). As you see in Scenario 2, the print resolution (ppi) affects the print size of an image. However, the printer resolution (dpi) does not affect the print size of the image; it affects the density of the ink dots on the print. Generally, the higher the dpi, the smoother the colors appear on the print. However, higher dpi uses more ink and requires a longer time to complete the print job.

10 OPTIMIZING THE FINAL IMAGE FOR THE WEB

The three image file formats currently supported by Web browsers are JPEG, GIF, and PNG. Each format has its characteristics that work best for different types of images. In addition, each employs different compression algorithms to compress the file size.

⏚ Worksheet: JPEG Compression Artifact Look at the impact of JPEG compression artifact on different digital images, and learn when and why an image may be or should not be saved in JPEG format.

The *JPEG* format works best with continuous-tone images with a broad color range and subtle color and brightness variations, such as photographs and images with gradients. JPEG supports 24-bit color (millions of colors). JPEG compression is a lossy compression method, which means it loses image data in order to make the file size smaller.

A highly compressed JPEG image tends to blur the image detail and shows a visible artifact around the high-contrast edges. For example, note the noises around the dark area in Figure 27d comparing to the same region of the uncompressed image shown in Figure 27b. Notice that the solid color areas in the original uncompressed image also no longer appear to be continuous solid color blocks in the JPEG images.

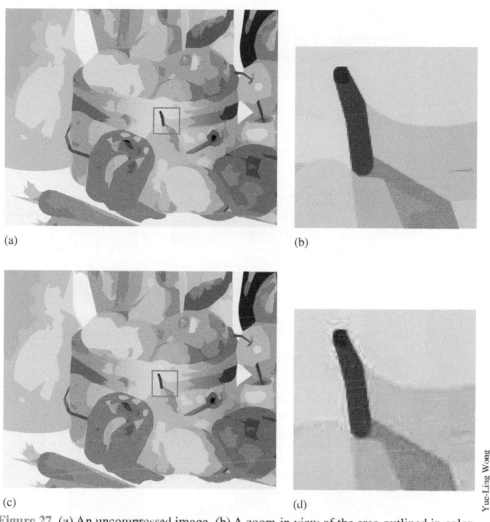

(a)

(b)

(c)

(d)

Yue-Ling Wong

Figure 27 (a) An uncompressed image. (b) A zoom-in view of the area outlined in color in image (a). (c) A highly compressed JPEG image of (a). (d) A zoom-in view of the area outlined in color in the JPEG image (b) showing the JPEG artifact. ▦ This image can be found on the insert.

The *GIF* format uses a palette of up to 256 colors (8-bit color depth) to represent the image, and it also supports background transparency. The GIF format works well for images with solid colors such as illustrations, logos, and line art. GIF images also can be created as animated sequences and saved as animated GIF files.

GIF files use a lossless compression. However, if an original image has more than 256 colors, you will need to reduce the number of colors in order to save the image as a GIF file. Some colors in such images will be altered when they are saved in the GIF format. Figure 28a shows a a screenshot of Photoshop's Save For Web & Devices

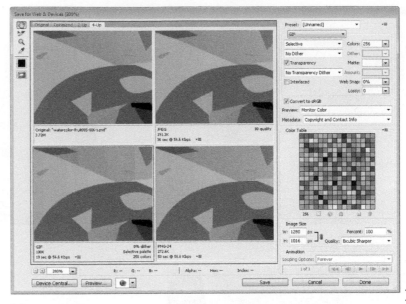

(a)

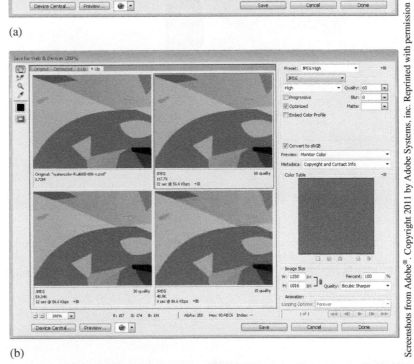

(b)

Figure 28 Adobe Photoshop CS5's Save for Web & Devices dialog box, displaying four versions of the image side by side. (a) The original uncompressed image, JPEG, GIF, and PNG. (b) The original uncompressed image and three different JEPG settings. (*continued*)

dialog box, where you can adjust settings for saving an image in different Web formats. For GIF files, you can choose a preset palette or customize the colors to be included in the palette. The GIF version in the upper-right in Figure 28c shows bands of solid colors in the gradient. It is because the original image has more than 256 colors and the

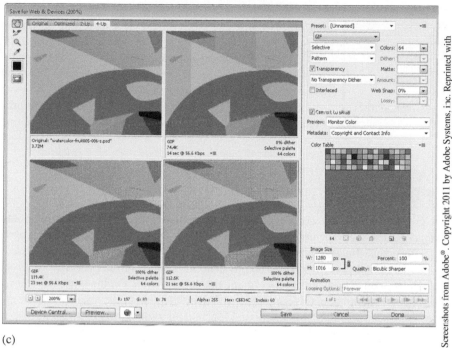

(c)

Figure 28 (*continued*) (c) The original uncompressed image (upper left) and three different GIF settings.

colors in the gradient that are outside of the palette are mapped to the closest color on the palette. In gradient areas, neighboring pixels have similar colors. The colors that are similar are mapped to the same color. At some points in the gradient when the colors are changing more and more, the neighboring pixels eventually are mapped to a different color. This causes the banding effect. When the number of colors in an image is reduced, the undesirable banding is not limited to gradient-filled areas; it can be in any areas with gradual color changes. The banding can be remediated by applying dithering. *Dithering* is a technique to simulate colors that are outside of the palette by using a pattern of like-colored pixels. The two GIF versions in the second row in Figure 28c are applied with dithering—each with a different dithering pattern. The undesirable banding effect in the gradient is reduced. If a Web image needs to have more than 256 colors, choose the PNG-24 or JPEG format.

The PNG format has two options: PNG-8 and PNG-24. Like the GIF format, the *PNG-8* format uses up to 256 colors to represent the image. Like the JPEG format, the *PNG-24* format supports 24-bit color. However, unlike the JPEG format, the PNG format uses a lossless compression and support transparency. There is no undesirable compression artifacts in PNG images. However, an image saved in PNG-24 format often has a larger file size than if it is saved in JPEG format.

> ◈ Downloadable Figure 28 The effects of different Web image settings on the example image shown in Figures 28a–c may not show up very well on the printed page in the text. Figures 28a–c are available on the text's Web site for you to take a closer look.

Adobe Photoshop CS5's `Save For Web & Devices` dialog box (Figure 28) lets you preview different optimization settings before you save your images into a JPEG, GIF, or PNG. It also shows the estimated file size and download time for a specified network connection speed. Figure 28a shows a comparison of JPEG, GIF, and PNG. Figure 28b shows three sets of different JPEG settings with the original uncompressed image. Figure 28c shows three sets of different GIF settings.

11 WORKING WITH VECTOR GRAPHICS PROGRAMS

Vector graphics programs work differently from image editing or photographic editing programs because the basic units that they are dealing with are different. Images are represented with pixels. Image editing programs such as Adobe Photoshop are pixel based. An image can be edited pixel by pixel. The physical dimensions of the print size of an image depend on its pixel dimensions and its image resolution in ppi. On the other hand, a vector graphic is not made up of pixels but mathematical description of the graphic. Vector graphics programs, such as Adobe Illustrator and Flash, deal with objects or shapes made up of paths, points, strokes, and fills.

11.1 Paths and Points

A *path* is a mathematical description of an abstract line or curve. It is defined by a set of points, called *anchor points* (Figure 29). A path can be open (Figure 29a) or closed (Figure 29b). Each point has *direction handles or tangent handles*. The curviness and the tangent at each point are controlled by its handle's length and angle, respectively (Figure 30).

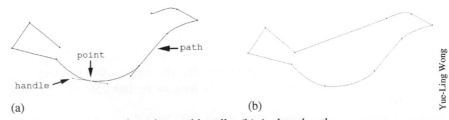

Yue-Ling Wong

(a)   (b)

Figure 29 (a) An open path, point, and handle. (b) A closed path.

There are two types of anchor points: corner points and smooth points. A *corner point* appears sharp and angular. Its handles have zero length. In vector graphics programs, a corner point does not have handles. Corner points (shown in color in Figure 31) are used for creating straight segments. A *smooth point* has direction handles to let you adjust the tangent and curviness at the point.

(a) (b) (c)

Figure 30 (a) and (b) The length of the handle controls the curviness of the path. (c) The direction of the handle controls the tangent at the point.

Figure 31 A path with corner points (colored).

In most vector graphics programs, one of the tools for creating paths is called the Pen tool. You use the Pen tool to define points for the path. In Adobe Illustrator and Flash, simply clicking with the Pen tool places a corner point. To create a new smooth point with the Pen tool, click-drag (i.e., drag while holding down the mouse button) and you can pull out the handles of the new point. A handle has two sides, each of which can be adjusted separately. For example, in Adobe Illustrator and Flash, you can ALT-drag (Windows) or Option-drag (Mac OS) using the Subselection tool on one of the handles to break their dependency, like the middle anchor point shown in Figure 32. In addition, corner points can be converted to smooth points at any time, and vice versa, by using the **Convert Anchor Point tool**.

Figure 32 The direction handles of the middle anchor point are broken out and can be adjusted independently.

DRAWING PATHS WITH THE PEN TOOL

The shape of a path is defined by these aspects:

- The position of each point
- The length of the handles of each point
- The direction of the handles of each point

The Pen tool lets you click-drag to create and adjust the handles while you are creating new smooth points. Many people who are new to the Pen tool often find it difficult to draw a path this way because the shape of a path is made up of multiple points and, on top of this, each point has those three aspects you need to determine.

Don't forget that the Pen tool also lets you simply click (instead of click-drag) to create corner points. You can convert corner points to smooth points later and adjust their handles at any time. This means that you can break up the complex task into multiple, simple stepwise tasks.

The following instructions intend to help you get started with the Pen tool by dealing with one aspect of a smooth point at a time.

Before drawing a path on the computer, do some planning first:

1. Once you have the shape in mind, sketch it out on paper. Suppose you want to draw a path as in Figure 33.

Figure 33 An example path that will be drawn.

2. Decide where to put the anchor points and figure out the minimum number of anchor points for the job. If the path is an open path, then each of the two ends of the path needs to have an anchor point.

   To decide where the anchor points are, look for the sharp change of direction. Keep in mind that a C-shaped segment can be created using only two smooth points (Figure 34).

Figure 34 A C-shaped curve can be created using only two smooth points.

The path shown in Figure 33 is an open path. Thus, each of the two ends of the paths will have an anchor point. There is a sharp change of direction in the middle. Thus, we can add one more anchor point there, as in Figure 35. Note that the whole path is basically made up of two C-shaped segments.

Figure 35 Decide the positions of the anchor points.

3. Eyeball the tangent of each anchor point on the curve and sketch it on paper. It will serve as a guide for you to adjust the direction of the anchor points' tangent handles.

   Returning to the example, the tangent for each point can be sketched out, as in Figure 36.

Figure 36 Eyeball the tangent for each anchor point and sketch it out on paper.

Once you have a sketch, drawing it in your vector graphic application program will be easy.

Activity/Exercise

1. Use the Pen tool to create all corner points, as in Figure 37, based on your sketch. Only worry about the position of each anchor point for now. Do not worry about the curvature at each point.

Figure 37 Create a path with corner points first.

2. After you have finished creating a path with all the corner points, convert those points that need to be smooth points using the Convert Anchor Point tool. Then, adjust each handle based on your sketch.

As you are getting more familiar with the Pen tool and using it more often, you may prefer the click-drag method because it saves the step of converting corner points to smooth points.

11.2 Strokes and Fills

A path does not have a physical appearance—line width or color—until the path is stroked with a specified line style, width, and color (Figures 38a and 38b). The vector graphics program may be set up to stroke the path by default. If so, whenever you create a path, it will be stroked with a line. If you set the *stroke* to none, the path will still be there, but you do not see it unless it is being selected and it will not be printed out.

A line style does not have to be a standard solid line. It can have an appearance of natural media, such as a dry paint brush like the one shown in Figure 38c. It can also be a custom defined style, such as the fish brush in Figure 38d.

A *fill* is a color, pattern, or gradient inside a shape defined by a path. Usually, fills also can be applied to open paths (Figure 39a) in addition to closed paths (Figure 39b).

11.3 Preset Shapes and Free-Form Drawing

There are tools to create common shapes such as ellipses, rectangles, polygon, stars, and spirals. Some programs also have a free-form drawing tool with which you can draw a

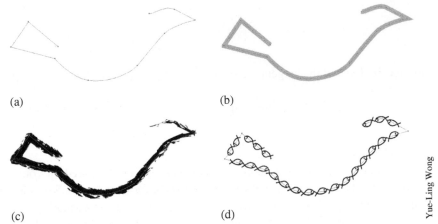

(a)   (b)

(c)   (d)

Yue-Ling Wong

Figure 38 (a) A path without stroke. (b) The path stroked with a solid line. (c) The path stroked with a line of charcoal brush style. (d) The path stroked with a line of custom brush style of a small fish.

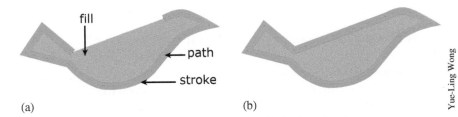

(a)   (b)

Yue-Ling Wong

Figure 39 Path, stroke, and fill. (a) An open path. (b) A closed path.

free-form path with a continuous stroke without manually defining the points. However, a free-form path is still made up of points; they are generated by the program.

11.4 Selection Tool

There are two basic selection tools in a vector graphics program: (1) the **Selection tool** in Adobe Illustrator and Flash, which lets you select the whole object; and (2) the **Subselection tool** in Flash or **Direct Selection tool** in Illustrator, which lets you select the points and their handles. Using the Selection tool, you can select the whole object and move, rotate, or scale it as a whole. With the Subselection or Direct Selection tool, you can alter the shape of an object by moving the points or their handles.

11.5 Layers, Effects, and Filters

Like many image editing programs, vector graphics programs also support layers that help you organize and manage the content. For example, you can toggle the visibility and the locking of a layer.

In addition, effects and filters, such as blur and drop shadow, that are available in image editing programs also are available in vector graphics programs. Some effects soften the edges of vector graphics to make them look more like bitmap images.

> ◈ **Example: Adding an Organic Feel to a Vector Graphic** This example demonstrates adding an organic feel to a vector graphic by using the following tools:
>
> - Filters
> - Gradient mesh
> - Importing bitmapped images
> - Clipping mask

11.6 Creating Complex Shapes Using Boolean Tools

Most vector graphic programs let you create complex shapes by performing ***boolean operations*** (such as union, subtract, and intersect) on overlapping simple shapes. For example, the ***Pathfinder tool*** (`Window > Pathfinder`) in Adobe Illustrator lets you merge, divide, trim, crop, outline, and minus overlapping shapes to create new shapes. To demonstrate the divide effect, in each of Figures 40a–c, one of the overlapping shapes is in thicker outline to show

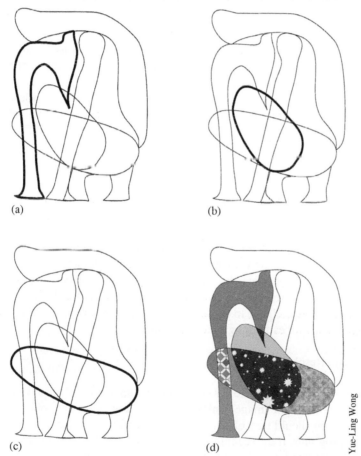

(a) (b) (c) (d)

Yue-Ling Wong

Figure 40 (a)–(c) An overlapping simple shape is in thicker outline to show you its original shape before applying a Pathfinder operation. (d) After the divide operation, the three overlapping shapes are divided into individual shapes that can be filled with different colors and patterns. (*continued*)

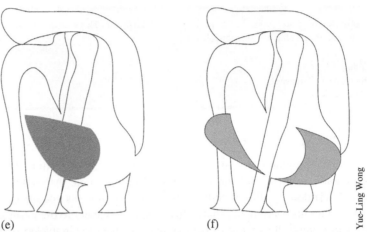

(e) (f)

Yue-Ling Wong

Figure 40 (*continued*) (e) The result after applying the crop operation on the two overlapping oval shapes. (f) The result after applying the minus back operation on the two overlapping oval shapes.

you its original shape. These three overlapping shapes are then selected to apply with the divide operation using Pathfinder. The shapes are divided up into individual shapes, which now can be filled with different fills and strokes independently (Figure 40d). These individual shapes also can be repositioned, resized, or deleted independently. Figure 40e and Figure 40f show the result after applying the crop and minus back operations, respectively, on the two overlapping oval shapes.

12 SUMMARY

In general, there are two ways to acquire digital images: scanning a picture and digital photography.

To determine the scanning resolution (dpi), you need to first determine the final image's pixel dimensions. How you determine the final image's pixel dimensions depends on what the final image is intended for—the Web or print. If it is intended for print, then the pixel dimensions of the image can be calculated by multiplying the image's intended physical dimensions and its intended printing resolution (ppi). If the final image is for the Web, then its pixel dimensions are estimated relative to the screen resolution of the intended display device.

The equation used for estimating scanning resolution is:

$$\text{Scan Resolution (in dpi)} = \frac{\text{Pixel Dimension (in pixels)}}{\text{Scan Source Dimensions (in inches)}}$$

If you are scanning a picture, make sure the scan resolution and color mode are appropriate for the way you will use the image. Unless the scanned image is not going to be retouched or edited at all, you should turn off auto sharpening, which is often enabled by default in many scanner programs. If the scanning software lets you look at the histogram of the scan preview, make sure you are assigning the appropriate tonal range to the scan. It is best to optimize the tonal range and correct any significant color problems during the scanning process. This is because once you have scanned the picture, any image editing afterward will not be able to recover the color information that got clipped off during scanning.

There are several steps in image retouching in general. Although not all of the steps are necessary, the order of these steps is important:

1. Crop and straighten the image.
2. Remove dirt and dust.
3. Adjust the overall contrast or tonal range of the image.
4. Remove color cast.
5. Fine-tune specific parts of the image.
6. Sharpen the image.

The term *megapixel* is commonly used to describe the resolution capability of a digital camera. A megapixel refers to one million pixels. With the same printing resolution (ppi), an image with more megapixels can be printed at a larger size than the one with fewer megapixels. Digital cameras that support more megapixels do not necessarily offer a higher image quality. Other factors, such as the optics of the camera and how the image data from the sensor is processed, also determine the quality of digital photographs. This chapter shows you that for printing at 150 ppi, the print dimensions are about 45 square inches per megapixel. These numbers can be interpreted as follows:

- At 150 ppi, about 7.6 inches $\times$ 5.7 inches per megapixel for a print of 4:3 width:height ratio
- At 150 ppi, about 8.2 inches $\times$ 5.4 inches per megapixel for a print of 3:2 width:height ratio

The physical print size of an image depends on two factors: its pixel dimensions and the print resolution. The following equation shows the relationships among these three variables:

$$\text{Print Dimension (in inches)} = \frac{\text{Pixel Dimension (in pixels)}}{\text{Print Resolution (in pixels per inch or ppi)}}$$

You can adjust the print resolution (ppi) to suit the print dimensions. Be careful not to unknowingly resize the image's pixel dimensions. In Photoshop, the Resample Image option in the Image Size dialog box lets you specify if you want to alter the image's pixel dimensions in changing the image size settings. Unchecking the Resample Image option will preserve the pixel dimensions of the image when adjusting the physical print size and print resolution.

The two basic and essential tools in digital image editing are selection and layers. Selection tools allow you to limit the editing to the selected area. Various selection tools are available for different selection tasks. Layers allow you to organize components of an image. You can rearrange their stacking order, adjust opacity, and blend with other layers.

If the image is intended for the Web, then the image needs to be saved in the JPEG, GIF, or PNG format. The JPEG format works best with continuous-tone images with a broad color range and subtle color and brightness variations, such as photographs and images with gradients. JPEG images use a lossy compression. A highly compressed JPEG image often appears blurry and shows undesirable artifacts due to compression. GIF images work well for images with solid colors, such as illustrations, logos, and line art. GIF images also can be created as animated sequences and saved as animated GIF files. The PNG format has two options: (1) PNG-24 (24-bit color, like JPEG) works well with continuous-tone images, and (2) PNG-8 (8-bit color, like GIF) works well with solid colors. Unlike the JPEG format, the PNG format uses a lossless compression and support transparency. There is no undesirable compression artifacts in PNG images. However, an image saved in PNG-24 format often has a larger file size than if it is saved in JPEG format.

TERMS

anchor points
Background layer
boolean operations
brightness
CCD (charge-coupled device)
clipping mask
CMOS (complementary metal-oxide semiconductor)
color balance
Color Balance tool
color casts
contrast
Convert Anchor Point tool
corner point
Crop tool
Curve tool
Direct Selection tool
direction handles or tangent handles

digital single-lens reflex (D-SLR)
dithering
dpi (dots per inch)
drum scanners
enhanced resolution
Eraser tool
Eyedropper tool
fill
flatbed scanners
GIF
handheld scanners
Healing Brush
highlights, midtones, and shadows
histogram
Hue/Saturation tool
JPEG
Lasso tool
layer mask
layers

Layers panel
Magic Wand tool
Magnetic Lasso tool
Marquee tools
megapixel
Move tool
optical resolution
path
Pathfinder tool
Pen tool
PNG-24
PNG-8
Polygonal tool
Quick Mask mode
Selection tool
sheet-fed scanners
smooth point
stroke
Subselection tool
tonal adjustments
Unsharp Mask tool

LEARNING AIDS

The following learning aids can be found at the text's companion Web site.

Tonal Adjustments during Scanning

An interactive tutorial that explains and demonstrates why tonal optimization is necessary during scanning.

Worksheet: Making Sense out of Megapixels

This worksheet guides you in looking up digital camera specifications and understanding how to calculate megapixels to suit your needs.

Photography: Understanding Shutter Speed, Aperture, and ISO

This supplementary reading explains the meaning and determination of the shutter speed, aperture, and ISO.

Image Retouching (Lab)

Use the example image (available from the text's Web site) and practice the retouching steps discussed.

Understanding and Applying Histograms

There are two parts of this learning aid: an interactive tutorial and practice exercises. The tutorial explains how to interpret an image's histogram and make tonal adjustments using histograms.

To test your knowledge of histograms, check out the two interactive exercises:

Exercise I: Reading Histograms. Practice relating the appearance of a histogram to the image characteristics.

Exercise II: Improving Image Contrast and Brightness. Identify the problem of the image by examining the histogram, and then improve it.

Light Metering Emulation of Photography

This emulates photographing a still life and illustrates the relationship between spot-metering and the resulting image's midtone.

Understanding and Applying Curves for Color Adjustments

An interactive tutorial and exercises help you undertand the Curves tool for the image ajdustment.

Photoshop Basics: Selection

A screen-capture movie gives a quick demonstration of some of the selection tools in Photoshop. A worksheet exercise is also available.

Image Alteration (Lab)

Use the example images (available from the text's Web site) to practice selectively altering areas.

Photoshop Basics: Using Layers

A screen-capture movie gives a quick demonstration of commonly used features of the Layers panel in Photoshop. A worksheet exercise is also available.

Making Composites: Example 1—Replicating an Object in Its Environment

In this example, the final image (Figure 24b) contains an extra object—a humanoid chain sculpture—which is not in the original image (Figure 24a). This example demonstrates the following aspects of image editing.

- Application of selection
- Scaling with the perspective in mind
- Creation of shadows

Making Composites: Example 2—Recreating a Sky Background

In this example, the final image (Figure 25c) contains an artificial sky and is created by compositing two digital images (Figure 25a and b). The tools used to make the composite include:

- Layer blending mode
- Layer mask
- Layer style
- Filters
- Stamp tool
- Dodge tool

Optical Color Mixing in Pointillism, Dithering, and Inkjet Printing

An interactive demonstration on optical color mixing.

Downloadable Figure 28

The effects of different Web image settings on the example image shown in Figure 28 may not show up very well on the printed page in the text. Figures 28a–c are available on the text's Web site for you to take a closer look.

Worksheet: Image ppi versus Printer dpi

Learn the difference between the printer dpi and image ppi by:

1. Experimenting with how the image ppi affects the output dimensions of the image.
2. Experimenting with how the printer dpi affects the printing quality of the image.

Worksheet: JPEG Compression Artifact

Look at the impact of JPEG compression artifact on different digital images, and learn when and why an image may be or should not be saved in JPEG format.

_⊕ Worksheet: JPEG versus GIF versus PNG

1. Learn to optimize files in JPEG, GIF, and PNG formats and to adjust the compression settings to achieve a balance between the file size and overall image quality.
2. Learn the type of images that each of these file formats is most effective at compressing.

✧ Example: Adding an Organic Feel to a Vector Graphic

This example demonstrates adding an organic feel to a vector graphic by using the following tools:

- Filters
- Gradient mesh
- Importing bitmapped images
- Clipping mask

REVIEW QUESTIONS

When applicable, please select all correct answers.

1. What are the different types of scanners?

2. What is the method of acquiring digital images besides scanning?

3. Resampling an image is often referred to as _____.

   A. rotating
   B. scaling
   C. translating
   D. repositioning

4. Scaling an image usually deteriorates the image quality somewhat. In four sentences or less, explain why in terms of what happens to the pixels by scaling up and scaling down.

5. The Apple iPhone 4S camera can take digital photographs with pixel dimensions of 3264 × 2448 pixels.

   i. Show the math that the resolution capability of the camera is 8 megapixels.
   ii. Show the math that with these pixel dimensions, the physical dimensions of the printed image are about 10-inch × 8-inch if you print it at 300 ppi.

6. Suppose that you scan a 3-inch × 5-inch photograph in at a resolution of 300 dpi.

   i. What are the pixel dimensions of the scanned image? _____ × _____ pixels
   ii. What will the physical dimensions of the image be if you print it at 300 ppi, without altering the image's pixel dimensions? _____ inches × _____ inches
   iii. What will the physical dimensions of the image be if you print it at 600 ppi, without altering the image's pixel dimensions? _____ inches × _____ inches
   iv. What will the physical dimensions of the image be if you print it at 150 ppi, without altering the image's pixel dimensions? _____ inches × _____ inches
   v. **True/False:** You gain image detail if you print the image at 600 ppi as noted in (iii).
   vi. **True/False:** You lose image detail if you print the image at 150 ppi as noted in (iv).

7. **True/False:** When a digital image is printed, each image pixel is represented by one printer ink dot.

8. The "per inch" in the units dots per inch and pixels per inch is in _____.

   A. square inches
   B. linear inches

9. **True/False:** The optimization of tonal adjustment at the time of capturing images—scanning or digital photography—does not matter because you can always extend the tonal range of the image to any extent afterward in Photoshop to recover the missing color information.

10. Given here are the general steps of image retouching of a scanned image.

   i. Order the steps by labeling 1 through 6.

   _____ Adjust the overall contrast or tonal range of the image
   _____ Crop and straighten the image
   _____ Fine-tune specific parts of the image
   _____ Remove color casts
   _____ Remove dirt and dust
   _____ Sharpen the image

   ii. Explain your choice for the first step.
   iii. Explain your choice for the last step.

11. Suppose you want to scan part of a photograph to use in a digital collage. The part of the picture you want to scan is 2-inch × 2-inch on the photograph. You want this scanned piece to appear as 6-inch × 6-inch in the final collage that will be printed out at 300 ppi.

   If you scan the picture at a resolution insufficient to print it at a size of 6-inch × 6-inch at 300 ppi, you will have to scale up the scanned image, which will deteriorate the image quality and make it look pixelated.

   What is the minimal scanning resolution (dpi) you should use to scan this 2-inch × 2-inch area so that you do not have to resize the image to meet the printing requirement? Show your calculations.

   (*Tip*: First calculate the pixel dimensions of that piece of image needed in the final collage.)

12. What kind of images are GIF files most appropriate for?

   A. Images with big areas of solid colors   C. Images with lots of gradients
   B. Continuous-tone photographs

13. What kind of images are JPEG files most appropriate for?

   A. Images with big areas of solid colors   C. Images with lots of gradients
   B. Continuous-tone photographs

14. Shown in Figure 41 is a grayscale image and its histogram:

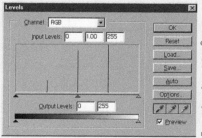

Figure 41 (a) A grayscale image. (b) The image's histogram.

Capturing and Editing Digital Images

i. Match each of the bars in the histogram to the color it represents. (Draw arrows linking each bar and the color in the grayscale image in Figure 41.)

ii. To maximize the contrast and tonal range of this image, what changes of the sliders should be made? Show the new positions of the sliders in the histogram provided in Figure 41.

iii. Figure 42 shows four different adjustments of the sliders made in the grayscale image's histogram. For each of the four image outlines in Figure 42, label the areas with the resulting grays. Specify whether it is black, white, or gray. If it is gray, estimate an RGB value for that gray.

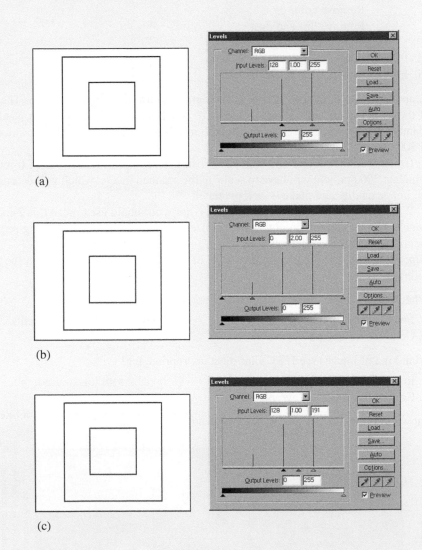

(a)

(b)

(c)

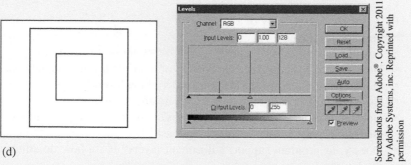

(d)

Figure 42 Four pairs of histograms and outlines of images, the colors of which are to be predicted based on the adjustment made in their histograms.

EXPLORING THE APPLICATIONS

1. Explore the selection tools of your image editing program. Use the Help menu or the user manual to find out the following how-to's. Write down the answers. Use your notes as a quick reference guide and refer to them as needed. (If your image editing program is Adobe Photoshop, there is a worksheet on selection tools of Photoshop available at the text's Web site.)

   • To select the whole image
   • To deselect
   • To inverse the selection
   • What are the different marquee tools available?
   • What are the different lasso tools available?
   • To add to a selection
   • To subtract from a selection
   • To select only an area intersected by other selections
   • To expand or contract a selection by a specific number of pixels
   • To feather the edge of a selection
   • To save a selection
   • To load a previously saved selection
   • How do you make selection by color?
   • Does your program have a Pen tool that allows you to draw paths to define the selection? If so, find out how it works.
   • Does your program let you make a selection by painting a "mask"? If so, find out how it works.

2. Explore the use of layers in your image editing program. Use the Help menu or the user manual to find out information for the following. Write down the answers. Use your notes as a quick reference guide and refer to them as needed. (If your image editing program is Adobe Photoshop, there is a worksheet on layers of Photoshop available at the text's Web site.)

   • To create a new layer
   • To delete a layer

- To duplicate a layer
- To toggle the visibility of a layer
- To rename a layer
- To adjust the opacity of a layer
- How do you move or scale the content of multiple layers simultaneously?
- How do you rearrange the stacking order of the layers?
- How does the stacking order of the layers affect the image?
- Does your program support layer masks? If so, how do layer masks work?
- Does your program support clipping mask? If so, how does clipping mask work?
- Does your program support adjustment layers? If so, how do adjustment layers work?

3. Explore your vector graphics program. Use the Help menu or the user manual to find out the information for the following. Write down the answers. Use your notes as a quick reference guide and refer to them as needed.

   - Find out the tools for creating paths
     - Pen tool
     - Free-form drawing tool
   - How do you add and delete points of a path?
   - How do you alter the curvature of a path?
   - How do you stroke a path?
   - How do you fill a shape?
   - Find out the selection tools for selecting whole objects and for selecting points and handles.
   - How do you create layers to organize the objects?
   - Find out the effects and filters available. Experiment with at least two.
   - Find out the tools that offer boolean operations on overlapping shapes to create new shapes.

4. Practice creating paths in a vector graphics program. If you are new to the vector graphics program, try to practice creating simple paths first, such as those shown in Figure 43, using corner points and smooth points. Use the same number of points as shown in the paths. The number of points on each of these paths is the minimum number of points for creating the path.

Yue-Ling Wong

Figure 43 Some simple paths to start with when starting to learn the Pen tool.

Also, practice editing the paths by moving the points and their handles. If you are getting familiar with the program, try creating more complex vector shapes using minimum number of points.

Fundamentals of Digital Audio

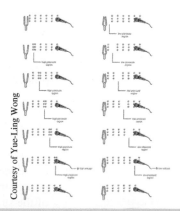

Courtesy of Yue-Ling Wong

Summary   Terms   Learning Aids   Review Questions

KEY CONCEPTS

- Sound wave
- Frequency and pitch
- Digitizing sound
- Sampling rate and bit depth of digital audio
- Nyquist's theorem
- Dynamic range
- Audio file size optimization
- MIDI

GENERAL LEARNING OBJECTIVES

In this chapter, you will learn

- The common terms in audio.
- The properties of sound waves.
- The basic steps of digitization—sampling and quantization—in digital audio.
- The effects of sampling rate and bit depth on digital audio quality.
- The meaning of *decibel*.
- The common file types for digital audio.
- The general strategies for reducing digital audio file sizes.
- The difference between digital audio recording and MIDI.

1 INTRODUCTION

Sound is an integral part of our everyday sensory experience. It is also an analog phenomenon. As is the case with most of our everyday sensory experiences, we seldom think of sound in its microscopic sense. However, in order to understand digital audio, you need to recognize the fundamental nature of sound as waves—the physics of sound. In this chapter we will explain and interpret the graphical depiction of sound as a **waveform**. A waveform serves as a means for us to "see" the information that we hear by providing quantitative properties of a sound, such as its amplitude and frequency.

2 THE NATURE OF SOUND WAVES

Sound is a wave that is generated by vibrating objects in a medium such as air. The vibrating objects can be the vocal cords of a person, a guitar string, or a tuning fork. Plucking a guitar string in the air causes the string to move back and forth. This creates a disturbance of the surrounding air molecules. When the string moves in one direction, it causes the air molecules to compress into a smaller space, raising the air pressure slightly in that region. The air molecules under higher pressure in that region then push the other air molecules surrounding them, and so forth. When the vibrating string moves in the reverse direction, it creates a gap between the string and the molecules. This lowers the air pressure in that region, causing the surrounding air molecules to move into that area. The displacement of air molecules propagates, radiating away from the string and causing periodic changes of air pressure—forming a sound wave. When this compression wave reaches your eardrums, it causes the eardrums to move back and forth. This sends a signal to your brain, which recognizes the changing air pressure as a sound. The harder you pluck the string, the greater the movement of the string, which causes greater displacement of the air molecules. This, in turn, causes higher pressure in the high-pressure region and lower pressure in the low-pressure region of the wave. When the string is plucked harder, the amplitude of the sound is higher and the sound is louder.

SOUND AS A MECHANICAL WAVE

Because the propagation of a sound wave in a medium relies on the mechanism of particle interactions, a sound wave is characterized as a mechanical wave. The implication of this property is that a sound wave does not propagate in a vacuum.

The motion of a particle in a sound wave is parallel to the direction of the wave. This type of wave is characterized as a longitudinal wave. Notice that it is the *motion* of the particles that propagates, not the particles themselves.

If you place a microphone in the path of the sound wave, the periodic air-pressure change will be detected by the recorder and converted into varying electrical signals. The changes of pressure in the propagating sound wave reaching the recorder are thus captured as changes of electrical signals over time. The sound wave can be represented graphically with the changes in air pressure or electrical signals plotted over time—a waveform (Figure 1). The vertical axis of the waveform represents the relative air pressure or electrical signals caused by the sound wave. The horizontal axis represents time.

A vibrating guitar string in the air causes the string to move back and forth, causing periodic changes of air pressure. The changes of pressure in the propagating sound wave reaching the recorder are captured as changes of electrical signals over time. The sound wave can be represented graphically with the changes in air pressure or electrical

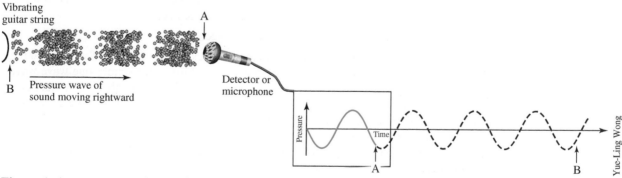

Figure 1 A pressure sound wave from a guitar string and its graphical representation.

signals plotted over time—a waveform. Be careful *not* to interpret the waveform as a representation of the sound wave in *space*. The picture on the left in Figure 1 is a picture of the air molecules in space. On the right is a graph over *time*. The air-pressure information at point B is *not* where time is zero on the waveform graph. Instead, the pressure information of point B has not yet propagated to the microphone; it would have been after point A has been recorded—about three more cycles to the right of point A on the waveform.

A waveform is a graphical representation of the pressure–time (not pressure-space) fluctuations of a sound wave. A sound wave propagates in space. The waveform matches the pressure changes in time at a fixed location. The crests correspond to the high pressure (compression of air molecules), and troughs correspond to the low pressure (rarefaction). The horizontal axis is time. However, looking at an illustration of a longitudinal pressure wave of sound placed side by side with its waveform can mislead you to think of the horizontal axis of the waveform as distance if you are not careful. Remember that the horizontal axis of a waveform is time, not distance. Let's re-emphasize two key points about a waveform:

> Sound as a Pressure Wave An illustration of a sound wave as a longitudinal air-pressure wave.

1. Be careful *not* to interpret sound wave as a wave that has crests and troughs, as in a transverse wave. Sound wave is a longitudinal wave, in which the particles of the medium (such as air molecules) move back and forth, not up and down, in the direction of the wave propagation.
2. Be careful *not* to interpret the waveform as a representation of the sound wave in *space*. Instead, the waveform graph represents the pressure changes over *time*.

Besides visualization of the pressure oscillation of the sound wave over time, a waveform can also give us information about the pitch and loudness of the sound. The following sections discuss how these two properties are measured and derived from the waveform.

2.1 Frequency and Pitch

A sound wave is produced by a vibrating object in a medium, say air. No matter what the vibrating object is, it is vibrating or moving back and forth at a certain frequency. This causes the surrounding air molecules to vibrate at this same frequency, sending out the sound-pressure wave. The *frequency* of a wave refers to the number of complete back-and-forth cycles of vibrational motion of the medium particles per unit of time. The common unit for frequency is *Hertz (Hz)* where the unit of time is 1 second.

$$1 \text{ Hz} = 1 \text{ cycle/second}$$

The period of a wave is the time for a complete back-and-forth cycle of vibrational motion of the medium particles. Shown in Figures 2a and b are two simple sine wave waveforms. If the tick mark on the horizontal axis marks the first second, then the frequency of the wave in Figure 2a has a frequency of 2 Hz, because it completes two cycles within 1 second. In Figure 2b, the wave has a frequency of 4 Hz.

Sound frequency is related to the *pitch* of the sound. Higher frequencies correspond to higher pitches. Generally speaking, the human ear can hear sound ranging from 20 Hz to 20,000 Hz.

Two notes that are an octave apart correspond to sound waves whose frequencies are in a ratio of 2:1.

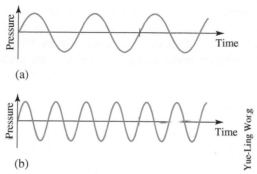

Figure 2 Simple waveforms representing two different frequencies: (a) lower frequency, (b) higher frequency.

2.2 Sound Intensity and Loudness

Sound intensity is related to the perceived *loudness* of a sound, but the two are not exactly the same. Sound intensity is often measured in *decibels (dB)*. A decibel is based on a ratio of a louder sound to a softer one. By definition,

$$\text{Number of decibels} = 10 \times \log (I_1/I_{ref})$$

(Equation 1)

where I_1 and I_{ref} are the two sound intensity values in comparison.

$$\text{Number of decibels} = 20 \times \log (V_1/V_{ref})$$

(Equation 2)

where V_1 and V_{ref} are the magnitudes of two electrical voltages or currents in comparison.

Notice that the decibel is not an absolute unit. It is an expression of a ratio of two values. More precisely, it is a logarithm of the ratio of two values. The general implication of this is that doubling the sound intensity means an increase of about 3 decibels. Or, a louder sound that causes twice the magnitude of the electric voltages or currents as a softer sound is about 6 decibels higher than the softer one. Why 3 and 6? Let's plug some numbers into the previous equations.

Say that you have a sound whose pressure wave produces an electrical signal V_1, and this pressure is double the pressure of some reference sound (V_{ref}). This means

$$V_1 = 2 \times V_{ref}$$

Plugging this relationship into Equation 2, we get:

$$\begin{aligned}
\text{Number of decibels} &= 20 \times \log (2 \times V_{ref}/V_{ref}) \\
&= 20 \times \log (2) \\
&\cong 20 \times 0.3 \\
&= 6
\end{aligned}$$

Similarly, plugging numbers into Equation 1 for doubling the sound intensity gives you 3 decibels. It may seem that this explanation presents more mathematics than you really need to know in order to work with digital audio editing programs. However, in many audio editing programs, the audio amplitude is measured in decibels. In addition, 3 and 6 decibels are given as preset values in amplification filters. Understanding what decibels mean and their relationship to audio signals helps you create predictable results in audio editing.

DECIBELS AND BELS

The unit called a *bel* was defined by scientists at Bell Labs to compare two power values. The unit was named after Alexander Graham Bell. By definition,

$$\text{Number of bels} = \log (P_1/P_0)$$

where P_1 and P_0 are the two power values in comparison. For sound, these can be considered the sound intensity.

A decibel (dB) is 1/10th of a bel (i.e., 1 bel equals 10 decibels.) So

$$\text{Number of decibels} = 10 \times \log (P_1/P_0)$$

Because power equals voltage times current, this relationship leads to the following (which we present without going into the mathematical derivation).

$$\text{Number of decibels} = 20 \times \log (V_1/V_0)$$

where V_1 and V_0 are the two voltage or amplitude values in comparison.

The threshold of hearing is the minimum sound-pressure level at which humans can hear a sound at a given frequency. It varies with frequency. Generally, 0 dB refers to the threshold of hearing at 1,000 Hz. Note that 0 dB does not mean zero sound intensity or the absence of a sound wave.

The threshold of pain is about 120 decibels, representing a sound intensity that is 1,000,000,000,000 (or 10^{12}) times greater than that of 0 decibel.

LOUDNESS VERSUS SOUND INTENSITY

The loudness of a sound is a subjective perception, but sound intensity is an objective measurement. Thus, loudness and sound intensity are not exactly the same properties.

To measure loudness, a 1,000-Hz tone is used as a reference tone. The volume of the reference tone is adjusted until it is perceived by listeners to be equally as loud as the sound being measured. Sound intensity, on the other hand, can be measured objectively by auditory devices independent of a listener.

The age of the listener is one of the factors that affect the subjective perception of a sound. The frequency of the sound is also a factor because of the human ear's sensitivity to different sound frequencies. The loudness of sound (as perceived by human ears) is only roughly proportional to the logarithm of sound intensity. However, in general, the higher the sound intensity, the louder the sound is perceived.

3 ADDING SOUND WAVES

A simple sine wave waveform represents a simple single tone—single frequency. When two or more sound waves meet, their amplitudes add up, resulting in a more complex waveform (Figure 3). The sound we perceive every day is seldom a single tone. The waveforms representing speech, music, and noise are complex waveforms that result from adding multiple waveforms of different frequencies. For example, Figure 4 shows a waveform of the spoken word "one."

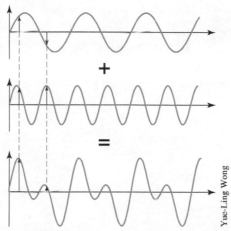

Figure 3 Addition of two simple sine wave waveforms results in a more complex waveform.

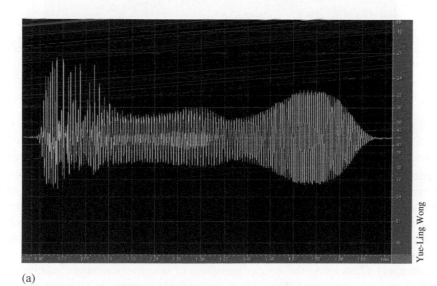

(a)

Figure 4 (a) A waveform of the spoken word "one." *(continued)*

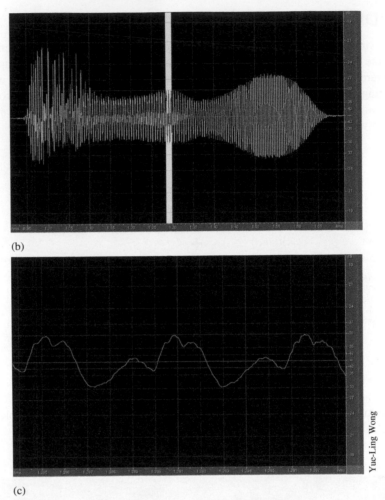

(b)

(c)

Yue-Ling Wong

Figure 4 *(continued)* (b) The highlighted segment to be magnified. (c) The zoomed-in view of the segment of the waveform.

The mathematical basis of the Fourier transform is discussed in the CS Module.

DECOMPOSING SOUND

When we record a sound, such as the spoken word "one" in Figure 4, the waveform recorded is a complex one. Can a complex wave be decomposed into its simple component parts—the different sine waves that make up the complex wave? Yes! One of the mathematical methods to accomplish this decomposition is called the Fourier transform.

But why would you want to decompose a complex wave into simple sine waves? The frequency of a simple sine wave can be determined easily. When you want to remove certain sounds that can be characterized by a range of frequencies, such as low-pitched noise, you can apply filters using the Fourier transform to selectively remove these unwanted sounds from a complex sound. These filters are available in many digital audio-processing programs and are used for breaking down a sound to remove unwanted frequencies.

4 DIGITIZING SOUND

A sound wave is an analog phenomenon. In a sound wave, the amplitude changes continuously over time. Like the process of digitizing any analog information, the process of digitizing sound involves sampling and quantizing an analog sound wave.

4.1 Step 1: Sampling

In the *sampling* step, the sound wave is sampled at a specific rate into discrete samples of amplitude values. The higher the sampling rate, the higher the accuracy in capturing the sound. However, a higher sampling rate will generate more sample points, thus requiring more storage space and processing time. To give you a feel

⊕ **Sampling and Quantizing in Digital Audio** An interactive tutorial illustrating the concepts of sampling and quantizing in digitizing a sound wave.

for the sampling rate for digital sound, the sampling rate for CD-quality audio is 44,100 Hz (i.e., 44,100 samples per second).

To keep the illustration simple and clear, our examples will use very low sampling rates. These rates are too low to be practical for digitizing sound in real life, but they are simple enough to demonstrate the point. Figure 5a represents a continuous sound wave signal. When we digitize the sound wave, we take discrete samples. Figure 5b shows a sampling rate of 10 Hz (that is, taking 10 samples of the pressure per second). Figure 5c shows a simple reconstruction of the wave by keeping the pressure value a constant between sample points. As you see, changes—crests and troughs—between any two sample points are missed.

The common reconstruction of an analog wave from the discrete sample points is not done by keeping the sample values constant between sample points, as shown in Figure 5c. Instead, it is usually done by interpolation of the sample points using mathematical algorithms to regenerate a smooth curve. However, no matter what technique is used to reproduce the sound wave, the number of sample points, and thus the sampling rate, is the limiting factor for the accuracy of the reconstruction.

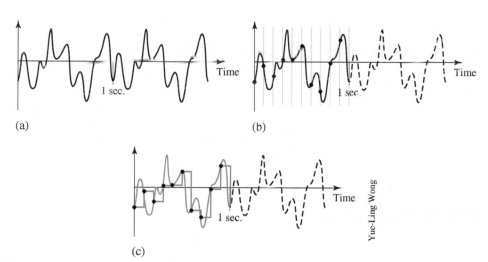

Yue-Ling Wong

Figure 5 (a) A theoretical continuous sound wave signal. (b) Ten samples of the pressure are taken per second—a sampling rate of 10 Hz. (c) A simple reconstruction by keeping the pressure value a constant between sample points.

What if we raise the sampling rate to 20 Hz? Figure 6a shows a sampling rate of 20 Hz, and Figure 6c shows a simple reconstruction of the wave. The reconstructed wave now looks closer to the original wave than the one sampled at 10 Hz does. As you see, a higher sampling rate can increase the accuracy of the reproduction of a sound wave.

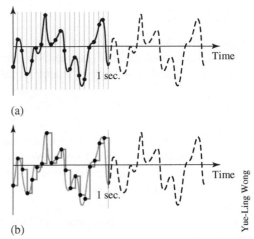

Figure 6 (a) A sampling rate of 20 Hz. (b) A simple reconstruction of the sound wave.

Because a higher sampling rate will produce more sample points, the file size of the resulting file will be larger. As in the 10-Hz example, changes—crests and troughs—between the sample points are still missed. This is an inherent limitation of the discreteness of digital data. No matter how high the sampling rate you adopt, there will always be missed points between those discrete sample points.

SAMPLING RATE VERSUS AUDIO FREQUENCY

Be careful not to confuse the sampling rate with the audio frequency. Both the sampling rate and the audio frequency are measured in Hertz (Hz), but they are not the same thing. The audio frequency relates to the pitch of the sound. The higher the frequency, the higher the pitch. The sampling rate refers to the number of samples taken per second for a sound wave. The sampling rate is a characteristic of the digitization process, but the audio frequency describes the sensory characteristics of the sound we perceive. The same sampling rate may be used for digitizing sounds of different audio frequencies. Conversely, the same sound may be digitized using different sampling rates to create different digital audio files.

4.2 Step 2: Quantizing

In the ***quantizing*** step, each of the discrete samples of amplitude values obtained from the sampling step will be mapped and rounded to the nearest value on a scale of discrete levels. Therefore, the more levels available in the scale, the higher the accuracy in reproducing the sound. For digital audio, having more levels means higher ***resolution***. However, higher resolution will require more storage space. The number of levels in the scale is expressed in ***bit depth***—the power of 2. For example, an 8-bit audio allows $2^8 = 256$ possible levels in the scale. To give you a feel of the bit depth for digital sound, CD-quality audio is 16-bit (i.e., $2^{16} = 65,536$ possible levels in quantizing the samples of amplitude values).

For demonstration purposes, we use 3-bit as an example, which is a scale of eight discrete levels. Again, 3-bit is not a practical bit depth used in real-life applications. The sampled data are mapped to the nearest level on the scale (Figure 7). Some samples may deviate more from their original amplitudes. With a low bit depth, data with different original amplitudes may be quantized onto the same level—for example, note the quantized sample points of the last six sample points in Figure 7b.

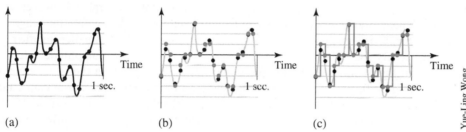

(a)　　　　(b)　　　　(c)

Figure 7 Quantizing with 3-bit resolution.

5 DYNAMIC RANGE

In the quantization step, a scale of discrete levels of amplitude values is used to map the sample points. The range of the scale, from the lowest to highest possible quantization values in the scale, defines the *dynamic range* for digitizing audio. In the quantization example of the previous section, where a scale of eight levels (3-bit samples) is used, the lowest level of the scale is placed at about the lowest amplitude of the sound wave and the highest level at about the highest point of the sound wave. The remaining six levels are equally spaced in between these two levels. This scale is extended to include the highest- and lowest-amplitude values of the sound wave. That is, none of the sample points is outside of this range. The scale, shown in Figure 8, covers a full amplitude range of the sound wave.

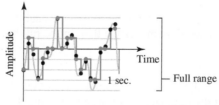

Figure 8 Quantization using a scale range equal to the full amplitude range of the sound wave.

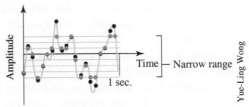

Figure 9 Quantization using a scale range narrower than the full amplitude range of the sound wave.

If the dynamic range is smaller than the full amplitude range of the sound wave (Figure 9), some data will be lost. The digitized sound wave will be "chopped" off at the limit of the range, causing clipping of the sound wave. Clipping is an undesirable effect because of loss of data. The clipped amplitude values are not recoverable. However, with a reduced dynamic range, the accuracy can be improved for the data within the range. This is an advantage, especially if most of the sample points are within a smaller middle region of the range. By sacrificing a small number of highest- and lowest-amplitude values, the accuracy of the majority of the sample points can be improved. In the simple example shown in Figure 9, you see that (with the same bit depth) reducing the dynamic range actually allows more subtle changes to be distinguishable (Figure 10). Instead of being quantized to the same value, some sample points can now be set apart on different levels.

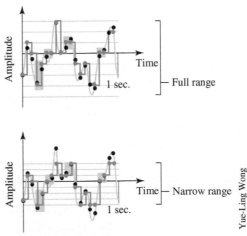

The dynamic range of a sound system refers to the range of the highest and lowest sound levels that the system can reproduce. In such context, a larger dynamic range is considered better because the sound system can then allow you to input audio components with wider ranges, and it can output the audio with minimal distortion.

Figure 10 The quantized data (shaded in blue) in which subtle changes become more distinguishable in the reduced dynamic range than in the full range.

What if you extend the dynamic range to more than the amplitude range of the sound wave? Then you will get the opposite result of reducing the dynamic range—the accuracy will be lost. As you see in Figure 11, the amplitude of the sound wave is now within only six levels of the range. So, although this extended dynamic range has eight quantization levels available, only six levels are utilized for this sound wave.

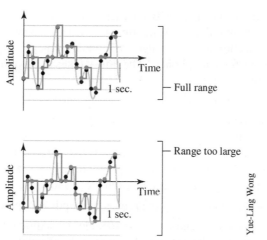

Figure 11 Comparing quantization using two ranges of scale: the full amplitude range of the sound wave, and one wider than the full amplitude range.

6 FILE SIZE, FILE COMPRESSION, AND FILE TYPES OF DIGITAL AUDIO

Higher sampling rate and bit depth always deliver better fidelity of a digitized file—whether it is an image or audio. So the recurring question may come up again: If higher sampling rate and bit depth give better fidelity and less degradation, then why shouldn't we always choose the maximum possible values? Well, the answer to this question is always the file size. Large file sizes require more storage space, longer processing time, and longer transfer time. Especially if the digital media files are created for use on the Internet, the network transfer time of a file is often a more important consideration than the storage space, which is becoming less expensive. The larger the file size, the longer it will take to download to another person's computer.

In addition to the sampling rate and bit depth, do not forget that the duration of the audio also affects the file size. Audio is a time-based medium. Audio files (such as speech and music) often require long, continuous playback. Therefore, the file size increases very rapidly with a higher sampling rate and bit depth. Let's look at an example of a 1-minute CD-quality stereo audio. A stereo audio has two *channels*—a left channel and a right channel. The bit depth of CD-quality audio is 16 bits per channel—16 bits per sample for each channel. Its sampling rate is 44.1 kHz—that is, 44,100 samples per second. The number of bits rquired to store a 1-minute CD-quality stereo audio is calculated as follows:

1 minute $\times$ 60 seconds/minute = 60 seconds

60 seconds $\times$ 44,100 samples/second = 2,646,000 samples

2,646,000 samples $\times$ 16 bits/sample = 42,336,000 bits

Because stereo audio has two channels, the total bit size = 42,336,000 bits $\times$ 2 = 84,672,000 bits.

To convert the bit size into bytes,

84,672,000 bits/(8 bits/byte) = 10,584,000 bytes $\cong$ 10 MB

Fundamentals of Digital Audio

As you see, it requires about 10 MB for each minute of CD-quality audio. An hour of such audio requires about 600 MB. At the time of writing, the average download speed of the 4G wireless connection is in the range of 2–6 mbps (megabits per second) for laptop modems and 1–2 mbps for smartphones.[1] The time it takes to download this 1-minute audio from the Web at 2 mbps would be

$$84{,}672{,}000 \text{ bits}/(2{,}000{,}000 \text{ bits/second}) \approx 42 \text{ seconds}$$

With 1 mbps on some smartphones, the time would be about 84 seconds, or almost 1.5 minutes. To reduce the download time, you may want to reduce the file size of the audio. The three general strategies of reducing a digital media file size are reducing the sampling rate, reducing bit depth, and applying file compression. As you see in the example, the equation for the audio file size calculation can be expressed as follows:

File size = duration × sampling rate × bit depth × number of channels

The equation for calculating audio file size includes an additional factor—the number of channels. Therefore, by examining the equation of audio file size calculation, you see four general strategies of reducing a digital audio file's size:

- Reduce the sampling rate
- Reduce the bit depth
- Apply compression
- Reduce the number of channels

Note that duration of the audio is also a factor in the equation for file size calculation. We do not include reduction of audio duration in the listed strategies because in most situations you want to keep the duration of the audio. However, keep in mind that the duration of the audio has a direct effect on the file size. You may want to remove the unnecessary silent segments in an audio file where possible. For example, most voice-over or speech contains unnecessary silence or pauses that may be removed to reduce the audio duration and thus the file size.

- **Reducing the number of channels.**
  Stereo audio has two channels. If you reduce a stereo audio file to mono—which becomes one channel—then you reduce the file size in half. This may suit speech and short sound effects for online games. Your decision to reduce the audio from stereo to mono is very much dependent on the nature of your project. Reducing a channel causes a noticeable difference unless your final product is expected to be listened to with a mono-speaker.
- **Reducing the sampling rate.**
  Reducing the sampling rate and bit depth sacrifices the fidelity of the digitized audio, which means it will sound less like the original. However, when working with digital media files, you often have to weigh the quality against the file size. When you do so, you often need to take into consideration both human perception of the medium and how you're going to use the audio.
  First, let's consider that the human ear can hear sound ranging from approximately 20 Hz to 20,000 Hz. The range varies with individuals and their ages. Not all people can hear the two ends of the average range. The human ear is most sensitive in the range of about 2,000 to 5,000 Hz, not the two ends of the range.
  Second, according to a rule called *Nyquist's theorem*, we must sample at least two points in each sound wave cycle to be able to reconstruct the sound wave satisfactorily.

[1] Mark Sullivan. "4G Wireless Speed Tests: Which Is Really the Fastest? AT&T, Sprint, T-Mobile, and Verizon: PCWorld's exclusive performance tests reveal which 4G network delivers the fastest data speeds." *PCWorld*. March 13, 2011. URL: http://www.pcworld.com/printable/article/id,221931/printable.html

In other words, the sampling rate of the audio must be at least twice that of the audio frequency—called a *Nyquist rate*. Therefore, a higher-pitch sound requires a higher sampling rate than a lower-pitch sound. In reality, the sound we hear, such as music and speech, is made up of multiple-frequency components. Then the sampling rate can be chosen as twice the highest-frequency component in the sound in order to reproduce the audio satisfactorily. Reducing the sampling rate sacrifices the sound quality of the higher frequencies.

The most common sampling rates you may encounter in a digital audio editing program are:

11,025 Hz: AM radio quality/speech
22,050 Hz: Near FM radio quality (common for multimedia projects)
44,100 Hz: CD quality
48,000 Hz: DAT (digital audio tape) quality
96,000 Hz: DVD audio quality
192,000 Hz: DVD audio quality

Based on the human hearing range and the Nyquist theorem, the sampling rate for CD-quality audio of 44.1 kHz is reasonable. But can we reduce the sampling rate, and if so, to what extent? Because the human ear is most sensitive in the range of about 2 to 5 kHz, then 11,025 Hz and 22,050 Hz seem to be reasonable sampling rates. 11,025 Hz causes more noticeable degradation to music than to speech because music has more higher-frequency components than speech. Because the human voice in speech normally does not exceed 5 kHz, the sampling rate setting of 11,025 Hz is reasonable for speech. Depending on the nature of your final product, a sampling rate setting of 11,025 Hz may also suit short sound effects (such as breaking glass and explosions), which may not require high fidelity.

So, how much can we lower the file size by reducing the sampling rate? From the file size equation, the file size can be reduced in the same proportion as the reduction of the sampling rate. In the example of 1 minute of CD-quality stereo audio, lowering the sampling rate from 44.1 kHz to 22.05 kHz will reduce the file size from about 10 MB to about 5 MB.

- **Reducing the bit depth.**

The most common bit-depth settings you may encounter in a digital audio editing program are 8 bit and 16 bit. According to the file size equation, lowering the bit depth from 16 to 8 reduces the file size in half. In the example of a 1-minute CD-quality stereo audio, lowering the bit depth from 16 to 8 will reduce the file size from about 10 MB to about 5 MB. Suppose the sampling rate of the audio has been lowered from 44.1 kHz to 22.05 kHz, creating a 5-MB file. Lowering the bit depth of this file from 16 to 8 will reduce the file size further, from 5 MB to 2.5 MB.

Eight-bit resolution is usually sufficient for speech. However, for music, 8-bit resolution is too low to accurately reproduce the sound satisfactorily. Our ears usually can notice the degradation in playback. Typically, 16-bit resolution is used for music.

- **Applying file compression.**

An audio file can be compressed to reduce the audio file size. Compression can be lossless or lossy. Lossy compression gets rid of some data, but human perception is taken into consideration so that the data removed causes the least noticeable distortion. For example, the popular audio file format MP3 uses a lossy compression that gives a good compression rate while preserving the *perceptible* quality of the audio by selectively removing the least perceptible frequency components of the audio. Keep in mind that a file compressed with a lossy compression method should not be used as a source file for further editing. To achieve the best result in editing an audio file, you should always start with a source file that is uncompressed or compressed with lossless compression.

No matter which file size reduction strategies you want to apply to your audio file, you should always evaluate the acceptability of the audio quality of the reduced file based on the nature of your audio project and weigh the quality against the file size limitation. The intended use of your final audio dictates the acceptability of trade-offs.

Even working within a limitation of file size, you should record or digitize with at least CD or DAT quality and then apply file size reduction strategies later, instead of digitizing at a lower sampling rate and bit depth in the first place. One reason is that compression algorithms are often designed to selectively remove data that will cause minimal impact on the audio quality perceivable by the human ear. Another reason is that by keeping a higher sampling rate and bit depth, you will have a choice of optimizing the file size by a combination of the file optimization strategies. You can weigh the file size reduction against the quality at that point. However, if you do not digitize at a high enough sampling rate or bit depth, you will get stuck with an unsatisfactory audio.

Many digital audio editing programs let you choose the format in which you want to save your audio file. The common file types are listed in Table 1. Some file types already dictate the compression option to be used. Others allow you to choose whether you want to compress the file, and possibly the compression options.

Generally, the intended use of your audio file determines the file format. You should take into consideration the following factors:

The information in Section 6.10 on streaming video and progressive download also apply to audio.

- **The file size limits.**
  If your audio is intended to be used on the Web, you may want to consider a file format that offers high compression or even a streaming audio file format to minimize the wait time to play your audio. Streaming audio means the audio will be played while it is being downloaded. The audio file does not have to be downloaded in its entirety before it can be played. However, it requires Internet connection during its playback.
- **The intended audience of your audio file.**
  How is your target audience going to listen to your audio? What equipment do they have? If they are listening on a computer, what is the operating system? If your audio will be played on multiple platforms, then the file should be a cross-platform format. If you want the audio to be played on a Web page without having to use external plug-ins, you may want to use HTML5 audio.
- **Keeping the file as a source file.**
  If you are keeping the file for future editing, then you should choose a file format that is uncompressed or uses lossless compression.

CLOUD COMPUTING FOR VIDEO AND AUDIO DELIVERY

The term "cloud" refers to the Internet and cloud computing refers to the technologies that provide computing services (such as storage, software, database access) to users via the Internet. For online storage, you can download your files onto your devices whenever needed. The downloaded video and audio files can be played back *from your devices*. For video and audio files, cloud-based service providers often also support streaming the media—the media is played back *over the Internet*. For example, Amazon Cloud Drive offers online storage and supports downloading and streaming of music files that are saved on your Cloud Drive. Apple iCloud lets you stream the music files stored on your iCloud and download them on any of your devices.

TABLE I	Common Audio File Types			
File Type	**Acronym For**	**Originally Created By**	**File Information and Type of Compression**	**Platforms and Additional Information**
.aiff	Audio Interchange File Format	Apple, adopted later by Silicon Graphics	Usually not compressed, but has a compressed version	Primarily for Mac OS; also supported on Windows
.wav		IBM and Microsoft	• Supports uncompressed and a number of different compression formats • One of the HTML5 audio formats	• Primarily for Windows, but can be used on other systems • Plays in Web browsers that support the .wav format of HTML5 audio; at the time of writing, the supported browsers are Firefox, Safari, Chrome, and Opera
.au and .snd	Also called μ-law or Sun μ-law format	Sun and NeXT	μ-law encoding compresses the file at a ratio of 2:1; slow decompression	Sun, Unix, or Linux operating system
.mp3	MPEG audio layer 3	Moving Pictures Experts Group	• Good compression rate with perceivably high-quality sound • One of the HTML5 audio formats	• Cross-platform; many digital audio players can play it • Plays in Web browsers that support the MP3 format of HTML5 audio; at the time of writing, it is supported by Safari, Internet Explorer (IE), and Chrome, but Chrome is dropping future support of MP3
.m4a	MPEG 4 format without the video data	Moving Pictures Experts Group	• AAC compression, same compression as the MPEG-4 H.264 without the video data • One of the HTML5 audio formats	Plays in Web browsers that support the AAC format of HTML5 audio; at the time of writing, it is supported by Safari, IE, and Chrome
.ogg or .oga		Xiph.Org Foundation	• Usually referred to as Ogg Vorbis format • Ogg is a container format • The audio codec is Vorbis	Plays in Web browsers that support the Ogg Vorbis format of HTML5 audio; at the time of writing, it is supported by Firefox, Chrome, and Opera
.mov	QuickTime movie	Apple	• Not just for video • Supports audio track and a MIDI track • Supports a variety of sound compressors • Files can be streamed with QuickTime Streaming Server • "Fast Start" technology also allows users to listen to media as it is being downloaded	Cross-platform; requires QuickTime player
.wma	Windows Media Audio	Microsoft		
.asf	Advanced streaming format	Microsoft	Proprietary compression algorithm	Primarily used with Windows Media Player

7 MIDI

So far in this chapter, we have been describing the digital audio of captured analog audio that is produced by the vibration of objects in air. The continuous fluctuation of pressure in a propagating pressure wave is captured by a device or microphone, then digitized by sampling and quantization. The audio can be speech, music, noise, or a combination of these.

There is another method of storing music information—in **MIDI** format. MIDI (Musical Instrument Digital Interface) is a communications protocol, not a physical object. It defines the common interface for electronic digital musical instruments to communicate with computers or other instruments or devices containing microprocessors. It specifies the configurations of cables and cable plugs and the format of the data.

Many electronic keyboards have built-in synthesizers. A MIDI keyboard looks like a small piano, but upon receiving a signal such as a key being hit, its electronic device synthesizes sound using its own internal microprocessor (i.e., computer). Computers also can be attached directly to a MIDI keyboard to capture the musical notes being played. There are also software programs that let you enter the notes directly via the computer's mouse and keyboard. The composed music also can be played through a MIDI keyboard that has a synthesizer.

MIDI signals are not digitized audio sample points but contain note *information* played with a virtual instrument. Such information includes the instrument being played, the note being played, the duration of the note, and how loud to play the note. Unlike the digital audio we have been describing in the previous sections of this chapter, MIDI music creation does not involve capturing and digitizing analog sound waves or any analog information. Therefore, it does not involve sampling and quantization; that is, there is no sampling rate or bit-depth option in creating and editing a MIDI file.

Compared to the sampled audio files, the MIDI format has both advantages and disadvantages. Its file size can be much more compact. For example, the file size of a 1-minute MIDI file can be about 2 KB, but, as you have seen in the file size calculations, a 1-minute, stereo, 16-bit audio with a sampling rate of 44.1 kHz is about 10 MB. If you convert this MIDI file into a 44.1 kHz, 16-bit, stereo digital audio file, it will become about 10 MB. MIDI music can be easily edited like sheet music by changing the notation, timing, and instruments.

The composed music of a MIDI file requires a synthesizer to play. The quality of the sound depends on the quality of the synthesizer that plays back the composed music. This can be a disadvantage because the actual sound produced by different synthesizers may differ even for the same note of the same instrument. The composed music you hear from your MIDI keyboard may not sound the same on your friend's MIDI keyboard or computer synthesizer. For example, QuickTime has its own selection of high-quality MIDI instruments and thus can play MIDI without an external MIDI synthesizer. But it sounds different from a full-fledged synthesizer.

The analogy for MIDI music versus digitized audio may be a cake recipe versus the baked cake. It is much easier and lighter to send a cake recipe to your friends. But how exactly the cake tastes and looks may vary depending on the exact ingredients your friends use—even the same temperature setting varies from oven to oven. On the other hand, a baked cake is more bulky to mail to your friends. But it ensures the cake's taste and look that you intend the recipient to experience.

8 SUMMARY

Sound is a wave that is generated by vibrating objects in a medium such as air. The vibrating objects can be the vocal cords of a person, a guitar string, or a tuning fork. An object vibrating in air creates a disturbance of the surrounding air molecules, causing periodic changes of air pressure—forming a sound wave.

No matter what the vibrating object is, the object is vibrating or moving back and forth at a certain frequency. This causes the surrounding air molecules to vibrate at this same frequency. The common unit for frequency is Hertz (Hz); 1 Hz refers to 1 cycle per second. The sound frequency is related to the pitch of the sound. Higher frequencies correspond to higher pitches.

Sound intensity is related to, but not exactly the same as, the perceived loudness of a sound. The loudness of a sound is a subjective perception, but sound intensity is an objective measurement. Sound intensity is often measured in decibels (dB). A decibel is based on a ratio of a louder sound to a softer one; it is not an absolute measurement.

When two or more sound waves meet, their amplitudes add up, resulting in a more complex waveform. The waveforms of the sound we perceive every day (such as speech, music, and noise) are complex waveforms that result when multiple waveforms of different frequencies are added together.

Like the process of digitizing any analog information, the process of digitizing a sound wave involves sampling and quantizing an analog sound wave. In the sampling step, the sound wave is sampled at a specific rate into discrete samples of amplitude values. The higher the sampling rate, the higher the accuracy in capturing the sound. But a high sampling rate will generate more sample points, which will require more storage space and processing time. In the quantizing step, each of the discrete samples of amplitude values obtained from the sampling step will be mapped to the nearest value on a scale of discrete levels. Therefore, the more levels available in the scale, the higher the accuracy in reproducing the sound. For digital audio, having more levels means higher resolution. But higher resolution requires more storage space for the same reason that higher bit depth for any digital media will increase the file size.

Audio files, such as speech and music, usually require long, continuous playback. Therefore, the file size increases very rapidly with higher sampling rate and bit depth. To reduce the file size, there are four general file optimization approaches: reduce the sampling rate, reduce the bit depth, apply compression, and reduce the number of channels. No matter which file size reduction strategies you want to apply to your audio file, you should always evaluate the acceptability of the audio quality of the reduced file based on the nature of your audio project, and weigh the quality against the file size limitation. The intended use of your final audio dictates the consideration of the acceptable trade-offs.

Even working within a limitation of file size, you will get better results by recording or digitizing at a sampling rate and bit depth that produce good audio quality and then apply file size reduction strategies later.

Another method of storing music information is in MIDI format. MIDI stands for Musical Instrument Digital Interface. MIDI files do not contain digitized audio sample points. Instead, they contain information about musical notes to be played with a virtual instrument. Such information includes the instrument being played, the note being played, the duration of the note, and how loud to play the note. Unlike digitized audio, MIDI music creation does not involve digitizing analog sound waves or any analog information. Therefore, there are no sampling rate and bit depth settings. MIDI music has the advantage of very small file size. Another advantage is that the music content can be edited easily. The disadvantage is that the sound depends on the synthesizer that plays back the composed music. Thus, you do not know how your MIDI file sounds on your target audience's devices.

TERMS

bit depth	loudness	resolution
channels	MIDI	sampling
decibels (dB)	Nyquist rate	sound intensity
dynamic range	Nyquist's theorem	waveform
frequency	pitch	
Hertz (Hz)	quantizing	

LEARNING AIDS

The following learning aids can be found at the text's companion Web site.

⌐ Sound as a Pressure Wave
An illustration of a sound wave as a longitudinal air-pressure wave.

⌐ Sampling and Quantizing in Digital Audio
An interactive tutorial illustrating the concepts of sampling and quantizing in digitizing a sound wave.

⌐ Audio Examples (a Short Musical Sound and a Sound Effect) with Various Combinations of Sampling Rate and Bit Depth
Audio examples of a short musical sound and an explosion sound effect with various sampling rates (44,100 Hz, 22,050 Hz, and 11,025 Hz) and bit depths (8 bit and 16 bit) are used to demonstrate the impact of sampling rate and bit depth on (i) the audio quality and (ii) the file size. Review questions on the impact of sampling rate and bit depth, the audio's waveforms, and frequency spectral views are also available.

REVIEW QUESTIONS

When applicable, please select all correct answers.

1. A sound with higher _____ is perceived to have a higher pitch.

   A. volume
   B. frequency
   C. fidelity
   D. sampling rate
   E. bit depth

2. The unit used for measuring _____ is Hertz (Hz).

   A. amplitude
   B. frequency
   C. sampling rate
   D. bit depth
   E. dynamic range

3. A waveform is a graphical representation of the _____ fluctuations of a sound wave.

  A. pressure–time
  B. space–time
  C. pressure–space

4. The horizontal axis of a waveform is _____.

  A. pressure
  B. distance
  C. time

5. The vertical axis of a waveform is _____.

  A. pressure
  B. distance
  C. time

6. True/False: Zero decibels is when there is absence of sound or no sound wave.

7. The _____ of a sound relates to the sound intensity or loudness.

  A. amplitude
  B. frequency
  C. sampling rate
  D. bit depth
  E. dynamic range

8. The _____ of a digitized sound affects the accuracy of the sampled amplitudes being stored.

  A. amplitude
  B. frequency
  C. sampling rate
  D. bit depth
  E. dynamic range

9. In digital audio, the number of sample points taken per second is called the _____.

  A. amplitude
  B. frequency
  C. sampling rate
  D. bit depth
  E. dynamic range

10. In digital audio, higher resolution means higher _____.

  A. amplitude
  B. frequency
  C. sampling rate
  D. bit depth
  E. dynamic range

11. How many levels of amplitude values does an 8-bit sound allow?

12. How many levels of amplitude values does a 16-bit sound allow?

13. Generally, the audio CD music sampling rate is _____ and bit depth is _____.

14. **True/False:** Eight-bit sound is generally considered to be more than adequate for recording music.

15. **True/False:** MP3 is a good file format to keep as a source file for further editing.

16. Which of the following are audio file formats?

    BMP   WAV   JPEG   AIFF   MP3   GIF

    JPG   PSD   TIFF   WMF

17. According to Nyquist's theorem, we must sample at least _____ points in each sound wave cycle to be able to reconstruct the sound wave satisfactorily. In other words, the sampling rate of the audio must be at least _____ of the audio frequency.

18. The reduction of a digital audio file size can be achieved by _____.

    A. reducing the sampling rate
    B. reducing the pitch of the audio
    C. reducing the bit depth
    D. reducing the amplitude of the audio
    E. applying file compression techniques

19. Higher _____ will result in larger file size.

    A. amplitude
    B. frequency
    C. sampling rate
    D. bit depth
    E. dynamic range

20. Reducing the sampling rate from 44.1 kHz to 22.05 kHz will _____.

    A. have no effect on the file size
    B. decrease the file size by half
    C. decrease the file size to about 1/22th
    D. decrease the file size to about 1/44th

21. Reducing the bit depth from 16 bit to 8 bit will _____.

    A. have no effect on the file size
    B. decrease the file size by half
    C. decrease the file size to 1/8th
    D. decrease the file size to 1/16th

22. Reducing the number of channels from two (stereo) to one (mono) will _____.

    A. have no effect on the file size
    B. decrease the file size by half
    C. decrease the file size to 1/5th
    D. decrease the file size to 1/10th

23. The MIDI standard specifies the _____.

    A. sampling rate for the synthesized sound
    B. bit depth for the synthesized sound
    C. configurations of cables and cable plugs
    D. format of the data

Fundamentals of Digital Video

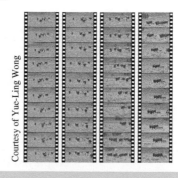

Courtesy of Yue-Ling Wong

Summary   Terms   Learning Aids   Review Questions

KEY CONCEPTS

- High-definition and standard-definition digital video
- Interlaced and progressive scan
- Overscan and safe zones
- Frame rate
- Frame size and frame aspect ratio
- Pixel aspect ratio
- Counting frames with timecode
- Data rate
- Video compression methods
- MPEG
- GOP, I-frame, P-frame, and B-frame
- Streaming video and progressive download

GENERAL LEARNING OBJECTIVES

In this chapter, you will learn

- The common terms in digital video.
- The common terms for DTV.
- The file formats of high-definition and standard-definition digital video.
- The relationship among frame size, frame aspect ratio, and pixel aspect ratio.
- How pixel aspect ratio affects the appearance of the video picture.
- How to read video timecodes.
- The difference between true streaming and progressive download.
- What GOP, I-frame, P-frame, B-frame, and the *M* and *N* parameters mean.
- How motion compensation and motion vector in MPEG compression work.
- The different implications of data rate and file size.
- How to determine the suitable video data rate for a playback target.
- The general strategies for video file size optimization.

1 THE NATURE OF MOTION AND BROADCAST VIDEO

In the natural world, we perceive motion as a continuous flow of events. It is a combination of visual, auditory, and temporal experience. Video cameras have long been available to capture motion on analog media, such as film, VHS tapes, and Hi-8 tapes.

Conceptually, motion is captured as a sequence of pictures at a constant time interval. Each picture is called a *frame*. How fast the pictures are captured or how fast the frames are played back is determined by the *frame rate*, which is measured in *frames per second (fps)*.

There are broadcast standards for digital video's resolution, color spaces, and frame rate to adhere to. The digital video standards have been influenced by the existing analog television broadcast standards. In order to understand the rationale behind digital video standards, it is necessary to learn about analog television broadcast standards.

1.1 Broadcast Standards

There are three sets of broadcast standards for analog color televisions. These standards pertain to the technical details of how color television pictures are encoded and transmitted as broadcast signals. Each standard is also characterized by its specific frame rate and the number of scan lines in each frame. These important attributes are translated into digital video standards. The number of lines in each frame in the analog broadcast standard is translated to the pixel height of a frame in digital video.

NTSC was named after the U.S. National Television Systems Committee, which designated this standard. It is used in North America, Japan, Taiwan, and parts of the Caribbean and South America. *PAL* stands for Phase Alternating Line, which refers to the way the signals are encoded. It is used in Australia, New Zealand, and most of Western Europe and the Asian countries. *SECAM* stands for Séquentiel Couleur avec Mémoire, which translates as sequential color with memory. It is used in France, the former Soviet Union, and Eastern Europe. The standards adopted in Africa and parts of Asia are mostly influenced by their colonial histories.

The implications of the scan lines in a frame will be discussed in Section 1.3.

Not all digital video formats have to conform to broadcast standards. Some digital video formats are intended mainly for computer playback—not for television. For example, QuickTime movies do not have to conform to a standard resolution or frame rate. On the other hand, videos intended for DVD playback need to conform to DVD-video standards, which are based on broadcast standards.

1.2 Frame Rate

Table 1 lists the frame rate of different systems. The frame rate for NTSC was originally 30 fps for black-and-white television broadcast. In order to accommodate additional color information for color pictures in the signal, the frame rate was lowered to 29.97 fps.

TABLE I	Frame Rates of Different Video Types
Video Type	Frame Rate (frames per second or fps)
NTSC	29.97
PAL	25
SECAM	25
Motion-picture film	24

1.3 Interlaced and Progressive Scan

A picture displayed on a television or a computer display is made up of horizontal lines. These lines are traced across the screen one line at a time. For example, a standard-definition NTSC frame contains 525 lines, of which about 480 are for the picture. A standard-definition PAL or SECAM frame contains 625 lines, of which about 576 are for the picture.

There are two ways to display a frame: by displaying the lines from top to bottom in one pass or two passes. Displaying all lines in one pass is called *progressive scan*. For the two-pass method, the set of the lines in the same pass (i.e., the set of even lines or odd lines) is called a *field*. The field containing the topmost scan line (i.e., the first scan line) is called the *upper field*, and the other

Video Display: Interlaced Scan versus Progressive Scan An interactive animation illustrates two-pass scanning in interlaced scan and one-pass scanning in progressive scan.

⊘ **Upper Field and Lower Field** An interactive demo shows the upper field and the lower field of a video frame.

◇ **Fast-Action Digital Video Showing the Interlace Artifact** A video clip of Figure 1 shows the comb-like interlace artifact.

⊘ **Video Recording: Interlaced Mode versus Progressive Mode** An interactive animation illustrates how the interlace artifact may be produced in fast-action videos.

field is the *lower field*. This display method of using two alternating fields is called *interlaced scan*. The first pass traces the one set of lines and the second pass traces the other set to fill in the alternating gaps left by the first pass. For example, for NTSC, the first pass traces the even-numbered lines and the second pass traces the odd-numbered lines.

For video shot in the interlaced mode, because the two fields in a frame are captured at a slightly different moment in time, discontinuities will become apparent for fast-moving objects. Such discontinuities appear as comb-like artifacts, such as in the areas of the soccer ball and the kicker's foot shown in Figure 1. The lower field of the frame is shown in Figure 1c and the upper field in Figure 1e. The interlace artifact usually is not apparent in normal playback. It is, however, discernible in slow motion or freeze frame.

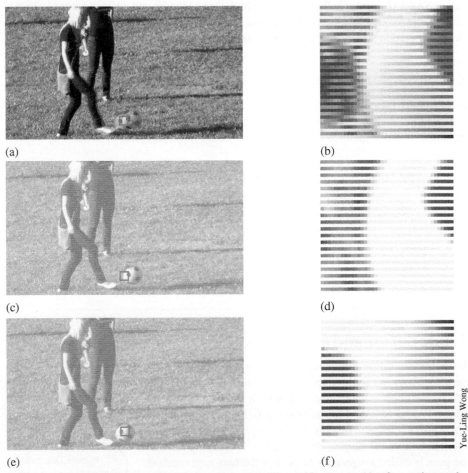

(a)　　　(b)

(c)　　　(d)

(e)　　　(f)

Yue-Ling Wong

Figure 1 (a) A digital video frame showing comb-like artifact caused by fast action and camera panning. (b) Close-up of the small outlined area in (a). (c) The upper field of the video frame. (d) Close-up of the small outlined area in (c). (e) The lower field of the video frame. (f) Close-up of the small outlined area in (e). ▪▪ This image can be found on the insert.

DEINTERLACE

The interlace artifact can be removed by discarding one field and filling in the gaps by duplicating or interpolating the other field (Figure 2). Either method will degrade the image quality.

During normal playback, the interlace artifact is not discernible. Deinterlacing is normally not necessary. However, if you need to capture a freeze frame and the interlace artifact is discernible, you may need to deinterlace the image.

(a)

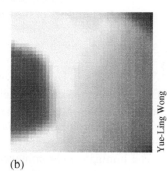
(b)

Yue-Ling Wong

Figure 2 (a) The video frame deinterlaced by eliminating the upper field and interpolating the lower field to fill in the gaps. (b) Close-up of the small outlined area. This image can be found on the insert.

1.4 Overscan and Safe Zones

When a video is displayed on a television set, the edge areas of the picture may not be displayed within the viewing area. The area that is outside of the screen is called the *overscan*. The signals are not "lost." For example, if you record a digital television program and play it back on a computer, you will see the whole image. If you watch a DVD movie on a computer, you can see a whole frame. However, if the same DVD movie is played on a television set, the content at the edges of the frame may not be seen on the screen due to the overscan.

As a consequence of overscan, if your target audience will be watching your video on consumer television sets, you should not place the important content too close to the edges when framing your shots. But how close is "too close"? There is no one exact number to fit all televisions, because the amount of overscanning is not consistent across consumer television sets.

There are two common guides that can help you frame your shots: the safe action area and the safe title area. The *safe action area* is where the significant action takes place. The *safe title area* is where you should place critical text titles and critical content. The safe title area is visible on the majority of television sets. In general, the safe action area occupies the center 90% of the frame size and the safe title area 80% (Figure 3). This means that the safe action area leaves approximately a 5% border all around the frame and the safe title area leaves about a 10% border around. For the frame shown in Figure 3, there is a person on the right edge of the frame walking to the left side of the frame. How much this person will show up within the viewing area on a television set depends on the television set.

If your video is created for viewing on computers, such as for Web playback, the entire frame will be displayed and the overscan will not apply.

Figure 3 (a) Outlines of the safe action area. (b) Outlines of the safe title area.

1.5 Color Format

RGB is a common color model used for still digital images, but for video, the luminance-chrominance color models are used (for example, *YUV* and *YIQ* color models). These color models divide color into one *luminance* (brightness) component (Y) and two *chrominance* (color or hue) components (U and V in YUV, or I and Q in YIQ).

The reason we introduce the analog broadcast's color models in this chapter is because the YUV color models are also used in the standards for digital video.

The luminance-chrominance color model was invented at the same time as color television for adding color signals to the television broadcast. By using this color model, the same signal could be used for both black-and-white and color television sets: the black-and-white television uses only the luminance (Y) signal, whereas the color set uses both the luminance and chrominance signals.

YUV was originally the color model for analog television broadcasts of the PAL system. YIQ is the model adopted by the National Television System Committee (NTSC) in the United States.

In addition, another luminance-chrominance model called YC_bC_r, which is closely related to YUV, is used in MPEG compression. MPEG compression is used in DVD videos and high-definition video formats. MPEG compression will be discussed later in this chapter.

RELATIONSHIPS BETWEEN RGB AND YUV/YIQ

The CS Module discusses the conversion between color spaces in detail. But to show you that the Y, U, and V, and Y, I, and Q, can be derived from RGB values, here are the equations:

$$Y = 0.299R + 0.587G + 0.114B$$
$$U = 0.492(B - Y) = 0.147R - 0.289G + 0.436B$$
$$V = 0.877(R - Y) = 0.615R - 0.515G - 0.100B$$

$$Y = 0.299R + 0.587G + 0.114B$$
$$I = 0.596R - 0.275G - 0.321B$$
$$Q = 0.212R - 0.523G + 0.311B$$

When you edit digital video, you do not need to explicitly set the color space to YUV or YIQ. If you create digital images for use in video, they can be kept in RGB format. The digital video editing program will convert the images to the correct color format.

2 SAMPLING AND QUANTIZATION OF MOTION

Each frame in a video is an image. Conceptually, in digital video, these images are digitized in a way similar to digital images by sampling and quantization. The image for each frame is sampled into a grid of discrete samples—the sampling process. Each sample becomes a pixel. The digital video frame size is still measured in pixels, as with digital still images. Each pixel is assigned a color value from a finite list of colors—the quantization process. The finite list of colors is within the video's color space.

In addition to the image frame, the sampling process also occurs in the temporal dimension of video. The sampling rate of the temporal dimension is the frame rate of the video. The higher the frame rate, the more accurate the motion that is sampled. However, for the same video duration, a higher frame rate also means more frames, which results in a larger file size.

3 MEASURING FRAME SIZE AND RESOLUTION OF DIGITAL VIDEO

Because digital videos are basically a sequence of digital images, many aspects of digital images can be applied to a video frame. For example, in digital video, the *frame size* is referred to as *resolution* and is measured in pixel dimensions.

However, unlike digital images, pixel per inch (ppi) is not really applicable in digital video. The ppi value matters *only* when the image is printed; ppi is meaningless for images intended for the Web or onscreen display. You never find the ppi attribute in digital video. The implication of this is that if you are creating a digital image to use in a digital video, you should set the image size based on the pixel dimension only; the ppi setting does not matter.

Another attribute used to describe the video frame size is its aspect ratio. As you will see in the following sections, a frame aspect ratio is not simply the ratio of its pixel width to its pixel height. This is because of an attribute called the pixel aspect ratio.

3.1 Frame Size

The *video frame size* (also referred to as resolution) is measured in the pixel dimensions of a frame—its width by its height, expressed in number of pixels. For example:

- For the **HDV** format—one of the high-definition video formats—there are two frame sizes at the time of this writing: 1,440 × 1,080 pixels and 1,280 × 720 pixels.
- For the **DVCPRO HD** format—another high-definition video format—there are three frame sizes at the time of this writing: 1,280 × 1,080 pixels, 1,440 × 1,080 pixels, and 960 × 720 pixels.
- For the NTSC standard-definition DV format, the frame size is 720 × 480 pixels. The frame size for a PAL standard DV frame is 720 × 576 pixels.

3.2 Frame Aspect Ratio

The *frame aspect ratio* is the ratio of its *viewing* width to height; it is not equivalent to the ratio of the frame's pixel width to height. For example, the frame aspect ratio for

The terms *DV* and *HDV* may appear to be simple abbreviations for *digital video* and *high-definition digital video*, respectively. However, DV format and HDV format refer to specific video standards. In this chapter, the terms *DV* and *HDV* refer to those specific standards, not shorthands for *digital video* and *high-definition digital video*.

high-definition digital video and high-definition TV (HDTV) is 16:9. For the standard-definition video, the frame aspect ratio for the standard format is 4:3, and the wide-screen format is 16:9 (Figure 4). Note that the grid in Figure 4 is used as a visual aid only to help you easily tell the width-to-height ratio. The grid cells are *not* representing the image pixels and the number of cells is *by no means* the number of pixels.

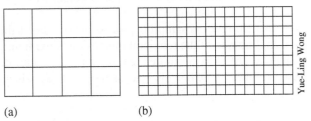

(a)   (b)

Figure 4 (a) A frame using an aspect ratio of 4:3. (b) A frame using an aspect ratio of 16:9.

3.3 Pixel Aspect Ratio

One of the supported frame sizes of HDV format is 1,280 × 720 pixels. The width-to-height ratio is 16:9, which matches the frame aspect ratio of high-definition video. The other frame size of HDV format is 1,440 × 1,080 pixels. Its width-to-height ratio does not match 16:9; it is 12:9. What is missing here?

The frame size and frame aspect ratio of different high-definition video formats are listed in Table 4.

Unlike digital image editing, in which images use square pixels by default, some video formats use nonsquare pixels to make up the frame. The shape of the pixel can be described by an attribute called ***pixel aspect ratio***. It is the ratio of a pixel's width to its height. For a square pixel, its pixel aspect ratio is equal to 1. A pixel aspect ratio of less than 1 depicts a tall pixel, whereas a pixel aspect ratio of greater than 1 depicts a wide pixel.

The pixel aspect ratio for HDV 720p is 1.0, and for HDV 1080i and 1080p is 1.333. Let's see if this makes sense for the HDV frame size and its frame aspect ratio.

- For HDV 720p that has a frame size of 1,280 × 720, its pixel aspect ratio = 1.0, because

$$\text{width : height} = 1,280 \times \text{pixel aspect ratio} : 720$$
$$= 1,280 \times 1.0 : 720 = 1,280 : 720 = 16:9$$

- For HDV 1080i and 1080p that has a frame size of 1,440 × 1,080, its pixel aspect ratio = 1.333 because

$$\text{width : height} = 1,440 \times \text{pixel aspect ratio} : 1,080$$
$$= 1,440 \times 1.333 : 1,080 = 1,920 \times 1,080 = 16:9$$

Similarly, for standard-definition DV format, the pixel aspect ratio for the wide-screen format (16:9) is 1.2, whereas the pixel aspect ratio of the standard format (4:3) is 0.9.

A video should be displayed on a system with the matching pixel aspect ratio; otherwise the image will be distorted. Figure 5 illustrates the effects of various pixel aspect ratios displayed on systems with different pixel aspect ratios. Figure 5a, d, and g show how video frames of pixel aspect ratios of 1.0, 0.9, and 1.2, respectively, are supposed to look when displayed correctly on a system with the pixel aspect ratio that matches

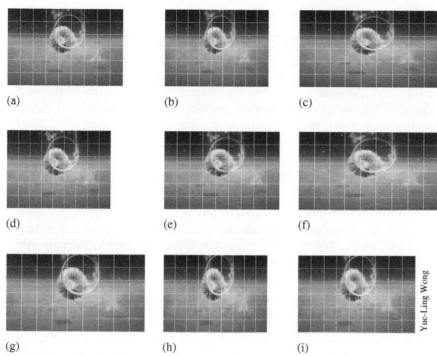

Yue-Ling Wong

Figure 5 The images in the first column show how they look when displayed with the correct pixel aspect ratio. The other six images demonstrate how they are distorted when displayed with an incorrect pixel aspect ratio. (a) A frame of pixel aspect ratio 1.0 displayed correctly. (b) A frame of pixel aspect ratio 1.0 displayed incorrectly with a pixel aspect ratio of 0.9; the ring is elongated vertically. (c) A frame of pixel aspect ratio 1.0 displayed incorrectly with a pixel aspect ratio of 1.2; the ring looks squashed. (d) A frame of pixel aspect ratio 0.9 displayed correctly. (e) A frame of pixel aspect ratio 0.9 displayed incorrectly with a pixel aspect ratio of 1.0; the ring looks slightly wider than it should. (f) A frame of pixel aspect ratio 0.9 displayed incorrectly with a pixel aspect ratio of 1.2; the ring looks squashed. (g) A frame of pixel aspect ratio 1.2 displayed correctly. (h) A frame of pixel aspect ratio 1.2 displayed incorrectly with a pixel aspect ratio of 0.9; the ring is elongated vertically. (i) A frame of pixel aspect ratio 1.2 displayed incorrectly with a pixel aspect ratio of 1.0; the ring is elongated vertically.

the frame's pixel aspect ratio. Figure 5b, c, e, f, h, and i show the distorted frames displayed on systems with a pixel aspect ratio different from the frame's intended pixel aspect ratio.

In short, a frame displayed on a system with a pixel aspect ratio larger than the frame's will stretch the image horizontally, whereas a frame displayed on a system with a smaller pixel aspect ratio will stretch the image vertically. The larger the difference between the frame's pixel aspect ratio and the system's, the greater the distortion.

Pixel Aspect Ratio An interactive demo shows you the effect of an incorrect pixel aspect ratio on an image.

SMPTE, founded in 1916, is an organization to develop standards in the motion picture industry. Its Web site is http://www.smpte.org.

4 COUNTING TIME IN DIGITAL VIDEO

Video editing requires precise synchronization and hence precise measurement of time. The smallest timing unit in video is a frame, which is usually only a fraction of a second. Therefore, our usual measurement of time in hours, minutes, and seconds is not precise enough for video. *Timecode* is used to number frames. *SMPTE* (Society of Motion Pictures and Television Engineers) video timecode, the most common timecode for digital video, numbers frames in hours, minutes, seconds, and frames. For example, 00:02:32:07 refers to the frame at 2 minutes, 32 seconds, and 7 frames.

There are two types of timecodes: drop frame and non-drop frame. For example, the following indicates video time at 0 hours, 2 minutes, 51 seconds, and 20 frames.

Drop-frame timecode	00;02;51;20
Non-drop-frame timecode	00:02:51:20

Notice that the drop-frame timecode uses semicolons, whereas the non-drop-frame timecode uses colons. This is how you can tell which timecode a system is using. The drop-frame timecode is preferable for the NTSC system.

WHAT IS THE DIFFERENCE BETWEEN DROP-FRAME AND NON-DROP-FRAME TIMECODES? WHY ARE THERE TWO TIMECODE FORMATS? HOW DO YOU CHOOSE WHICH ONE TO USE? DOES USING DROP-FRAME TIMECODE RESULT IN DELETING FRAMES FROM THE VIDEO?

To help you understand the need for two different timecodes, let's look at an analogous situation in our daily life—the purpose of leap years.

The time it takes for the Earth to orbit the Sun is about 365.242199 days, according to the Encyclopedia Britannica. Because it is not an exact number of days, we need leap years.

How does this work? A year is designated as 365 days because the number 365.242199 is closer to 365 than 366. However, this causes an inevitable slight shift of days—about a 0.24 day each year, or about 24 days for every 100 years. Without leap years, the seasons would shift. By adding one extra day to every fourth year, we get $(356 \times 3 + 366)$ days for four years, that is, an average of 365.25 days per year. This offsets the shift very closely.

Why do we need to offset the shift? It is because we want to keep the seasons at the same time of the year every year. But do we skip or delete time from our lives using leap years? No, of course not. We have the same amount of time no matter whether we have leap years or not; it is just a different way of counting days.

A similar situation arises with the NTSC-standard timebase. The NTSC-standard timebase is 29.97, not exactly 30 frames per second (fps). This fractional discrepancy will accumulate to make a significant difference between the actual frame duration and the time duration. Using the drop-frame timecode eliminates this error.

TABLE 2	**Examples of How the Drop-Frame and Non-Drop-Frame Timecodes Count Frames, Where the Length in Minutes Is Calculated by Dividing the Number of Frames by the Frame Rate**			
Number of Frames	Length (minutes) for 29.97 fps	Length (minutes) for 30 fps	Drop-Frame Timecode	Non-Drop Frame Timecode
1799	1.0004	0.9994	00;00;59;29	00:00:59:29
1800	1.001	1	00;01;00;02	00:01:00:00
17981	9.999	9.989	00;09;59;29	00:09:59:11
17982	10	9.990	00;10;00;00	00:09:59:12

When you use a drop-frame timecode, the program renumbers the first two frames of every minute except for every 10th minute. To demonstrate what this means, Table 2 shows the comparison of the two timecode formats with the length of video calculated based on different frame rates. For example, the drop-frame timecode increments from 00;00;59;29 to 00;01;00;02 in stepping one frame from the 1,799th frame to the 1,800th. The timecode skips 00;01;00;00 and 00;01;00;01—*renumbers two frames*—but *no* frame is actually discarded or dropped. On the other hand, the non-drop-frame timecode increments from 00;00;59;29 to 00;01;00;00.

For video of 29.97 fps, the 1,800th frame is actually a little longer than 1 minute; it is about 1.001 minutes (1,800/29.97). As you see, the drop-frame timecode 00;01;00;02 represents the duration of the 29.97-fps video more accurately than the non-drop-frame timecode 00:01:00:00.

However, the drop-frame timecode increments from 00;09;59;29 to 00;10;00;00 in stepping one frame from the 17,981st frame to the 17,982nd. The timecode now does not renumber any frame because it is the 10th minute—the first 10th. For the 29.97-fps video, the drop-frame timecode represents exactly the length of the video.

The discrepancy between the drop-frame and non-drop-frame timecodes seems very small. However, the discrepancy grows as the frame number progresses. If you have a separate audio created for the video, the discrepancy in video length will cause problems in synchronizing the separate audio track with the video.

In working with digital video editing programs, you need to choose a timecode format—drop frame or non-drop frame—for your project. However, you do not need to compute the timecode. The explanation provided in this section on how drop-frame timecode is computed is intended to help you understand the rationale to use the drop-frame timecode for the NTSC video and how it counts frames to maintain the time accuracy. It also helps you understand why some timecodes, such as 00;01;00;00 and 00;01;00;01, are skipped—not an abnormality. No frame is discarded in the process.

DROP-FRAME TIMECODE: WHY RENUMBER THE FIRST TWO FRAMES OF EVERY MINUTE? AND WHY SKIP THE RENUMBERING EVERY 10TH MINUTE?

It sounds complicated at first, but let's do a calculation to demonstrate the rationale behind it, so it does not seem complicated anymore.

Question

1. Why renumber the first two frames of every minute?

Let's first find out the number of frames in a video of exactly 1 minute.

- If the timebase for counting frames is 30 fps:

$$30 \text{ fps} \times 60 \text{ seconds} = 1{,}800 \text{ frames}$$

- If the timebase for counting frames is 29.97 fps:

$$29.97 \text{ fps} \times 60 \text{ seconds} = 1{,}798.2 \text{ frames}$$

For a 1-minute video clip, the frame difference between the 30 fps and 29.97 fps is:

$$1{,}800 - 1{,}798.2 = 1.8 \text{ frames, or } \textit{approximately two frames}$$

Now you see why the first *two frames* of every minute need to be renumbered in the drop-frame timecode for NTSC-standard timebase.

Question

2. Why does such renumbering skip every 10th minute?

At exactly 10 minutes, for 30 fps, it is the 18,000th frame. It is denoted as 10:00:00 in non-drop-frame timecode.

But if counted for 29.97 fps, the 18,000th frame is a little over 10 minutes—it is 10 minutes and 18 frames (18,000 frames/29.97 fps).

In the first 9 minutes, drop-frame timecode has already renumbered 18 frames (2 frames each minute) to offset the shift; 18 frames are the offset necessary for 10 minutes. Therefore, when it comes to the 10th minute, it should not renumber another two frames; otherwise, it will overcompensate.

5 DIGITAL VIDEO STANDARDS

5.1 Standard Definition

The term *DV* is often used as an abbreviation for *digital video*. However, **DV compression** or DV format refers to specific types of compression. For example, **DV25** is the most common DV compression for **standard-definition digital video**.

DV25 is used by many digital video camcorders. These camcorders compress the video directly inside the camcorder. The video you get on tapes is already compressed into DV format. Table 3 lists the specifications for the DV25 format.

DV25 compresses the video at a fixed data rate of 25 megabits per second (Mbps) for the visual component of the video—hence the 25 in its name. This means the video takes up 3.125 MB of storage space per second. The total data rate for video, audio, and other control information is about 3.6 MB per second. The color space and color sampling method for NTSC is YUV 4:1:1. For NTSC, the frame size of the video is 720 × 480 pixels, and the frame rate is 29.97 fps.

TABLE 3	Part of the Specifications of DV25 Format	
Pixel Dimensions	720 × 480 (NTSC)	
Frame Aspect Ratio	4:3	16:9
Pixel Aspect Ratio	0.9	1.2
Data Rate — Total (video + audio + control information):	3.6 megabytes per second (MB/s), i.e., about 4.6 minutes of video per gigabyte of storage space	
Video data only:	25 megabits per second (Mbps); compressed at a fixed rate of 5:1	
Color Sampling Method	YUV 4:1:1	
Audio Setting — Sampling rate and bit depth:	Two options: • 48 kHz, 16 bit • 32 kHz, 12 bit	

WHAT DOES YUV 4:1:1 MEAN?

While RGB is a common color model used in digital photographs or any still digital images, the common color model used in digital video is a luminance-chrominance model, such as YUV, to represent the color of each pixel. The Y component is the luminance (brightness). The U and V components are the chrominance (color or hue).

The human eye is more sensitive to changes of luminance than it is to chrominance changes. Digital video systems exploit this phenomenon to reduce the storage of information by using fewer bits to storing the chrominance components. In other words, some chrominance data will be discarded. This method is called **chroma subsampling** or **color subsampling**.

There are several subsampling formats, depending on the ratio of the chrominance information to be discarded. The format is designated with three numbers separated by colons, for example, 4:2:2, to represent the ratio of the Y-component to the two chrominance components, Y:U:V.

The full-color information for each pixel contains one sample each of Y, U, and V. Thus, there are a total of three samples per pixel related to color information.

4:4:4

The designation *4:4:4* means for each group of four pixels, four samples of the Y-component and four samples each of the two chrominance components will be stored—that is, a total of 12 samples for each group of four pixels. In other words, there is no saving in storage (no compression), that is, no subsampling.

4:2:2

The *4:2:2* subsampling method means that for every four pixels, it will use:

- 4 samples of Y
- 2 samples of U
- 2 samples of V

The need for using fewer bits to store the color information is much higher for digital videos than still digital images because a video file contains many frames resulting in a much larger file than a still image. Using the RGB model for digital videos would not have allowed us to take advantages of the human perception to reduce the file size.

The total of samples used for every four pixels is now reduced from 12 to 8. This means a one-third reduction in storage requirements.

This subsampling method is used in Digital Betacam video format.

4:2:0

The *4:2:0* subsampling method means that for every four pixels, it will use:

- 4 samples of Y
- 2 samples of either U or V

The total of samples used for every four pixels is now reduced from 12 to 6. This results in a 50% reduction in storage requirements.

The selection of U and V are alternated by scan lines. In one scan line, the samples from the U are used. In the next scan line, the samples from the V are used.

This subsampling format is used in HDV, MPEG-1, DVD MPEG-2, and PAL DV.

4:1:1

The *4:1:1* subsampling method means that for every four pixels, it will use:

- 4 samples of Y
- 1 sample of U
- 1 sample of V

The total of samples used for every four pixels is now reduced from 12 to 6. This means a 50% reduction in storage requirements.

This subsampling method is used in NTSC DV. The DV format is used in the miniDV digital video camcorder.

5.2 High Definition

Table 4 lists several common high-definition video formats. For example, the HDV format supports three picture formats: *720p*, *1080i*, and *1080p*. The number designates the pixel height of the frame size, and the letters "p" and "i" specify the video's scan type—progressive and interlaced, respectively. For the HDV format, the pixel dimensions for the 720p are 1,280 × 720 pixels and for the 1080i and 1080p are 1,440 × 1,080 pixels.

You may recognize these video format names because they are often displayed on the video cameras (Figure 6).

Although Table 4 seems to be a mere collection of independent factual information, commonalities among these specifications exist. For example:

- The frame aspect ratio is 16:9.
- The picture formats are 1,080 and 720; each can be either interlace or progressive.
- For the 1080 format, the supported frame sizes are 1,440 × 1,080 (with pixel aspect ratio of 1.333—wide pixel) and 1,920 × 1,080 (with pixels aspect ratio of 1.0—square pixel).
- For the 720 format, the supported frame sizes are 960 × 720 (with pixel aspect ratio of 1.333—wide pixel) and 1,280 × 720 (with pixels aspect ratio of 1.0—square pixel).
- The color sampling method is either 4:2:0 or 4:2:2.

The main differences between these formats are the video and audio compression, which combined, in turn, influence the data rate.

TABLE 4 Several High-Definition Video Formats

Format	Frame Dimensions	Aspect Ratio	Frame Rate (fps)	Picture Format	Color Sampling Method	Data Rate	Video Compression	Audio Setting
HDV	• 1,440 × 1,080 (displayed at 1,920 × 1,080) • 1,280 × 720	16:9	• NTSC: 29.97, 59.94 • PAL: 25, 50 • Film: 23.98	1080i 1080p 720p	4:2:0	2.5–14 MB/sec. depending on codec	MPEG-2: • Constant bit rate (CBR) • Uses I-, P-, and B-frames • GOP N = 15	• Sampling rate: 48 kHz • Bit depth: 16 • Encoded using MPEG-1 Layer 2 format with a data rate of 384 kbps
DVCPRO HD	• 1,280 × 1,080 (displayed at 1,920 × 1,080) • 1,440 × 1,080 (displayed at 1,920 × 1,080) • 960 × 720 (displayed at 1,280 × 720)	16:9	• NTSC: 29.97, 59.94 • PAL: 25, 50	1080i 720p	4:2:2	115 Mbps (i.e., 14.4 MB/sec.)	• Uses a variation of DV and DVPRO 50 codecs • Compression ratio = 8.6:1	• Sampling rate: 48 kHz • Bit depth: 16
AVCHD	• 1,920 × 1,080 • 1,440 × 1,080 (displayed at 1,920 × 1,080) • 1,280 × 720	16:9	• NTSC: 29.97 • PAL: 25 • Film: 23.98	1080i 1080p 720p	4:2:0	Average bit rate is 5–24 Mbps, depending on the camcorder brand and the quality setting on the camcorder	• Uses Advanced Video Coding (AVC) compression, or H.264 (also known as MPEG-4 part 10) • Uses I-, P-, and B-frames • Uses variable bit rate (VBR)	5.1-channel surround sound with Dolby Digital (AC-3) up to 7.1-channel surround sound (uncompressed)
AVC-Intra	• 1,920 × 1,080 • 1,440 × 1,080 (displayed at 1,920 × 1,080) • 1,280 × 720 • 960 × 720 (displayed at 1,280 × 720)		• NTSC: 29.97 • PAL: 25 • Film: 23.98		4:2:0 4:2:2	• 50 Mbps: For 1,440 × 1,080 and 960 × 720, and color sample ratio of 4:2:0 • 100 Mbps: For 1,920 × 1,080 and 1,280 × 720, and color sample ratio of 4:2:2	• Uses Advanced Video Coding (AVC) compression, or H.264 (also known as MPEG-4 part 10) • I-frame-only compression	4-channel uncompressed

Figure 6 High-definition video cameras of different video formats: (a) HDV, (b) AVCHD, and (c) DVCPRO HD.

One of the key differences between high-definition and standard-definition video is their frame size (resolution). To give you an idea of how the frame sizes of high-definition video differ from those of standard-definition video, Figure 8 shows a comparison of the frame sizes. Note that the pixel dimensions of a frame may be different from its viewing size because some high-definition digital video standards (for example, HDV 1080i and 1080p) and standard-definition DV use non-square pixels for displaying the frame.

HIGH-DEFINITION VIDEO PICTURE FORMAT NOTATION

When describing the high-definition video picture format, it is often written in a form such as 1080/60i or 720/30p. Figure 7 explains the notation.

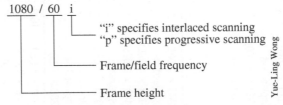

Figure 7 High-definition video picture format notation.

To give you a feel of the relative frame sizes of different digital video formats and how the different frame sizes may affect the details of the image, Figure 9 shows a comparison of the viewing frame sizes. Figure 9a is a frame from an 1080/60i video. Its pixel

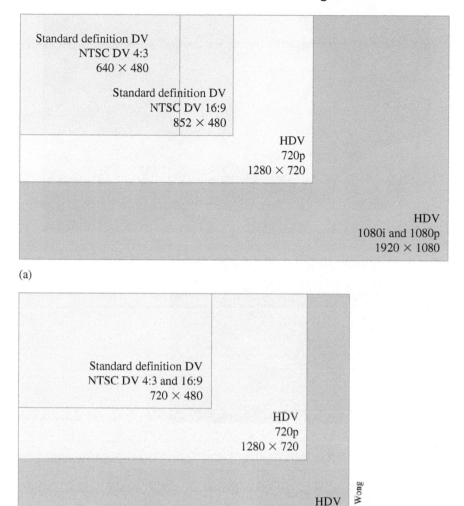

(a)

(b)

Yue-Ling Wong

Figure 8 Comparison of frame sizes of standard-definition and high-definition digital video: (a) Comparison by the viewing frame sizes. (b) Comparison by the pixel dimensions.

dimensions are $1{,}440 \times 1{,}080$. The figure shown is scaled based on its pixel aspect ratio to make the frame conform to the frame aspect ratio of 16:9. Figures 9b through 9d are scaled to show you how the frame would have looked if it was shot at the resolution for 720p, standard-definition DV 16:9, and standard-definition DV 4:3 format.

At the time of writing, in addition to high-definition camcorders that shoot video in one of the formats listed in Table 4, there are also digital SLR cameras that can take high-definition video at 1080p (in full $1{,}920 \times 1{,}080$ pixels) and 720p (in full $1{,}280 \times 720$ pixels) in addition to still pictures.

(a)

(b)

(c)   (d)

Figure 9 Frame size comparison: (a) A frame from a 1080i video. (b) The same frame in 720p format. (c) The same frame in standard-definition DV wide-screen (16:9) format. (d) The same frame in standard-definition DV standard 4:3 format.

5.3 Digital Television (DTV)

For more information about ATSC and its standard development, visit its Web site at http://www.atsc.org.

The signals of digital television (DTV) are broadcast over the air or transmitted digitally by a cable or satellite system. In order for the consumer to watch DTV, a decoder is needed to receive and use the signal, which is in digital form, to directly drive the digital TV set.

At the time of this writing, in the United States, *Advanced Television Systems Committee, Inc. (ATSC)*—an international nonprofit organization that develops voluntary standards

TABLE 5	The 18 ATSC Formats for DTV		
	Frame Size	**Display Aspect Ratio**	**Frame Rate and Scan Mode**
SDTV	704 × 480	16:9	24p
			30p
			60i
			60p
		4:3	24p
			30p
			60i
			60p
	640 × 480	4:3	24p
			30p
			60i
			60p
HDTV	1,920 × 1,080	16:9	24p
			30p
			60i
	1,280 × 720	16:9	24p
			30p
			60p

for DTV—has developed a total of 18 DTV formats: 12 formats for *standard-definition television (SDTV)* and 6 for *high-definition television (HDTV)*.

Table 5 lists the 18 formats. Again, the letter "p" or "i" next to the frame rate designates the scan mode: "p" for progressive and "i" for interlaced. The frame rate for the progressive scan refers to frames per second. The number for the interlaced scan is actually in fields per second—for example, 60i refers to 30 frames per second, because each interlaced frame consists of two fields. HDTV uses MPEG-2 format and has a higher resolution than both the traditional analog TV and SDTV. The frame aspect ratio of all six HDTV formats is 16:9.

The Federal Communications Commission (FCC) mandated that all television stations be capable of broadcasting digital television (DTV) by February 17, 2009. In order for consumers to watch DTV, there are several equipment requirements on different parties, for example:

For more information, visit http://www.dtv.gov/consumercorner.html.

- TV stations need production and transmission equipment for DTV programs.
- Consumers need equipment for reception of the DTV signals.

6 FILE TYPES OF DIGITAL VIDEO

Many digital video editing programs let you choose the video format in which you want to export your video file. The common file types are listed in Table 6. The file types often already dictate the available compression method.

Fundamentals of Digital Video

Generally, the intended use of your video file determines its file format. Here are several considerations:

- *The file size and data rate limits.*
  - If your video is intended for use on the Web, then you may want to consider a file format that offers high compression or a streaming video file format.
  - If your video is intended for CD-ROM or DVD-DOM playback, you will need to consider a data rate that can be handled by your target audience's computers.
  - If your video is intended to be DVD-video, then you need to export it into DVD MPEG-2 that fits on a DVD disc.
- The *intended* **audience of your video file.**
  - If your video will be played on multiple platforms, then the file format should be cross-platform. The cross-platform formats (see Table 6) include Apple QuickTime, MPEG, Flash Video, and RealVideo.
  - If your video is intended for the Web playback, you may want to consider exporting your video into HTML5 video formats. At the time of writing, there are three HTML5 video formats: MP4 (.mp4, .m4v), Ogg Theora (.ogg and .ogv), and WebM (.webm).
  - What equipment is your target audience going to use to watch your video?
    - If they are playing it on mobile devices, then you may want to consider using HTML5 video for the Web playback.
    - If they are playing it on a set-top DVD player, then you need to make a DVD-video.
    - If they are playing it on computers, then what kind of computers are they using—older or newer? This dictates the data rate for your video.
- **Files that are intended to be** *source files* **for future editing.**

  You may want to choose a file format that is uncompressed (provided that the frame size is small, the video duration is extremely short, say less than 30 seconds, and

TABLE 6   Common Video File Types for Windows and Mac OS

File Type	Acronym For	Originally Created By	File Information and Codecs	Platforms
.mov	QuickTime movie	Apple	• Not just for video, but there is also audio-only QuickTime • Also supports MIDI • Files can be streamed with QuickTime Streaming Server • "Fast Start" technology also allows users to play the video as it is being downloaded • Common codecs include H.264, Sorenson Video, Animation, and PlanarRGB	Apple QuickTime player, which is available for Mac and Windows
.avi	Audio Video Interleave	Intel	Common codecs include Microsoft RLE and Intel Indeo Video	Primarily used on Windows but Apple QuickTime player can play AVI files
.rm	RealVideo or RealMedia	Real Systems	• Supports very high degree of compression • Allows you to choose the compression level in terms of network connection speed • Files can be streamed with RealServer	• Cross-platform • Requires Real player

(Continued)

TABLE 6 *Continued*

File Type	Acronym For	Originally Created By	File Information and Codecs	Platforms
.wmv	Windows Mcdia	Microsoft		Primarily used with Windows Media Player
.divx		DivX, Inc	• Uses DivX codec, which is based on MPEG-4 • Popular format for movies because of the high image quality and small file size • AVI is a common container file format, i.e., a video using DivX codec may have the file extension .avi	• May require downloading DivX codec (available for Mac OS and Windows) for playback and creation of DivX videos because not all computers have the codec pre-installed • Windows Media Player v11.0 comes with DivX codec
.mpg .mpeg	MPEG	Motion Picture Experts Group	• DVD-compliant MPEG-2 is used for DVD-video • Blu-ray compliant MPEG-2 is one of the supported Blu-ray formats	Cross-platform
.flv	Flash Video	Adobe	• Supports progressive download from a Web server • Can be streamed If the file is hosted on Adobe Flash Media Server Video codecs include: • Sorenson Spark • On2 VP6: This also supports alpha channel, which means the video can have transparency	• Cross-platform • Requires Adobe Media Player to play • Can be embedded in Flash SWF files • A popular video format used by Web sites, such as YouTube
.f4v	Flash Video	Adobe	• Builds on MPEG-4 Part 12[1] • Supports H.264/ACC-based content	• A newer Flash Video format than .flv • Cross-platform • Requires Adobe Media Player to play • Can be embedded in Flash SWF files
.mp4	MPEG-4	Moving Pictures Experts Group	• Video codec: H.264 • Audio codec: AAC • One of the HTML5 video formats	Plays in Web browsers that support the MP4 format of HTML5 video; at the time of writing, it is supported by Safari and Internet Explorer (IE)
.ogg or .ogv		Xiph.Org Foundation	• Video codec: Theora • Audio codec: Vorbis • One of the HTML5 video formats • Compared to the other two HTML5 video formats, it has lower quality for the same file size	Plays in Web browsers that support the Ogg Theora format of HTML5 video; at the time of writing, it is supported by Firefox, Chrome, and Opera
.webm		An open source video format from Google	• Video codec: VP8 • Audio codec: Vorbis • One of the HTML5 video formats	Plays in Web browsers that support the Ogg Theora format of HTML5 video; at the time of writing, it is supported by Firefox, Chrome, and Opera

[1]http://www.adobe.com/devnet/f4v.html.

you have enough disk storage) or allows lossless compression. This is not a common option because an uncompressed video or even a video using lossless compression will require a large amount of storage space.

- Most video compression methods are lossy but some allow you to specify the quality of the compressed video. You may want to set a high quality level when exporting videos that are intended to be used as source files for future editing.

7 DIGITAL VIDEO FILE SIZE AND OPTIMIZATION

The file size of an uncompressed high-resolution image can be very large. For example, the file size of an uncompressed 3,000-pixel × 2,000-pixel, 24-bit image is 18,000,000 bytes, or about 17 MB.

For digital video, the frame size is not as large. For example, the frame size for the HDV 1080i and 1080p is 1,440 × 1,080 pixels. However, video is comprised of a sequence of images (24 to 30 frames per second), which quickly increases the file size. For example, a 1-minute video at a frame rate of 30 fps comprises 1,800 frames! Even if each frame takes up only 1 MB, 1,800 frames will equal almost 2 GB of data!

Let's look at the size of a video with the following properties:

- 1,440-pixel × 1,080-pixel frame size
- 24-bit color
- 30 fps
- 1-second length
- Audio: stereo (two channels)
- Audio: 48,000-Hz sampling rate and 16 bit

The *uncompressed* file size can be computed as follows:

For the video:
Total pixels in each frame:

$$1,440 \times 1,080 \text{ pixels} = 1,555,200 \text{ pixels/frame}$$

File size in bits for each frame:

$$1,555,200 \text{ pixels/frame} \times 24 \text{ bits/pixel} = 37,324,800 \text{ bits/frame}$$

File size in bits for 1-second video:

$$37,324,800 \text{ bits/frame} \times 30 \text{ frames/second} \times 1 \text{ second} = 1,119,744,000 \text{ bits}$$

File size in bytes:

$$1,119,744,000 \text{ bits} / (8 \text{ bits/byte}) = 139,968,000 \text{ bytes} \cong \textbf{133 MB}$$

For the audio:
File size of an uncompressed audio file:

Sampling rate × length of the audio × bit depth × number of channels

$$= 48,000 \text{ samples/second} \times 1 \text{ second} \times 16 \text{ bits/sample} \times 2$$
$$= 1,5 36000 \text{ bits}$$
$$= 1,5 36000 \text{ bits} / (8 \text{ bits/byte})$$
$$= 192,000 \text{ bytes}$$
$$\cong \textbf{188 KB}$$

Thus, a 1-second uncompressed video would require 133 MB + 188 KB (video + audio) of storage space, which is about 133 MB!

7.1 Data Rate

The file size is one of the considerations in deciding video export options for your final video—a larger file requires more storage space. But there is another important factor: its data rate, which is related to the smoothness of the video playback. The **data rate**, also referred to as bit rate because it is reported in bits per second, refers to the amount of video data to be processed per second. The average data rate of a video is calculated by dividing the file size by the total length or duration of the video in seconds. If the data rate of a video is too high for the computer to handle, its playback will be choppy. This may become less of a concern because computers nowadays are fast enough to handle typical videos. However, for a video on the Web delivered by streaming or pseudostreaming, if its data rate is too high for the viewer's network connection, the video will have to pause frequently to wait for the data.

Streaming and pseudostreaming allow a Web video to start playing while it is being downloaded. See Section 10.

VIDEO FILE SIZE VERSUS DATA RATE

Video file size and data rate are closely related, but they do not have the same implications. File size pertains to the *total* amount of the data. A large file size requires more disk space and longer transfer time.

Data rate refers to the amount of data to be processed *per second*. Hence, a very long video, even with a low data rate, can have a large file size. Data rate affects the smoothness of the video playback. If the data rate is too high for a computer to handle, the data will not be processed fast enough for continuous playback. The playback will be choppy.

HOW DO I DETERMINE IF THE DATA RATE OF MY VIDEO CAN BE HANDLED BY THE AUDIENCE'S DEVICES?

The properties of a video, such as data rate, file size, and frame size, can be looked up in the QuickTime Player by selecting Window > Show Movie Inspector. The Movie Inspector shown in Figure 10a shows that the file size (data size) of the QuickTime movie example is 98.94 MB, and its average data rate is 31.77 mbits/sec (mbps or megabits per second). But where does the 31.77 mbits/sec come from? Here is how the average data rate is calculated:

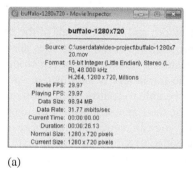
(a)

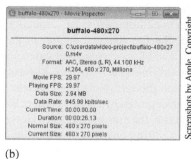
(b)

Figure 10 QuickTime Player's Movie Inspector showing the data size and data rate of two QuickTime movies with different frame sizes and compression options.

The movie's data size (i.e., file size) is 98.94 MB. The data rate is reported in mbits/sec. Let's first convert the data size from MB into mbits: 1MB = 1,024 KB, 1 KB = 1,024 bytes, and 1 byte = 8 bits. Thus, the number of bits for 98.94 MB is: 98.94 MB × 1,024 KB/MB × 1,024 bytes/KB × 8 bits/byte = 829,968,875 bits For data rate calculation, 1 mbits = 1,000 kbits and 1 kbit = 1,000 bits. Thus, 829,968,875 bits = 829,968,875 bits / (1,000 bits/kbit) / (1,000 kbits/mbits) = 829.97 mbits The movie's duration is 26.13 seconds. Thus, the data rate is: 829.97 mbits / 26.13 seconds = 31.8 mbits/sec

At the time of writing, the speed of the typical residential broadband connection is in the range of 3–20 mbits/sec. The average download speed of the 4G wrieless connection is in the range of 2 – 6 mbits/sec for laptop modems and 1 – 2 mbits/sec for smartphones.[2] The data rate of the example movie is much higher than these ranges. It will have to pause frequently during playback to wait for data while it is being downloaded.

Figure 10b shows the movie information of the same movie but with a smaller frame size (480 × 270 vs. 1,280 × 720 of the original) and different compression options. The data rate is now 945.98 kbits/sec (or 0.946 mbits/sec). For a typical residential broadband or 4G wireless connection, this video should play without having to pause to wait for data while it is still being downloaded. Its data rate also falls within the range of mobile 3G connection speeds (about 1 mbits/sec), and thus it also can play smoothly while being downloaded on 3G mobile devices.

Because video is comprised of a sequence of images and audio, the strategies for reducing the file size of digital images and audio are also applicable for digital video.

The strategies for reducing image file sizes are: reducing the pixel dimensions, lowering the bit depth, and compressing the file. Similarly, the strategies for reducing audio file size are: reducing the audio sampling rate, reducing the audio bit depth, compressing the file, and reducing the number of channels.

There is an additional type of video file compression that is different from those of image file compression. This type of compression method exploits the temporal nature of video. The general concepts of video file compression will be discussed in the next section.

Let's first look at how the general strategies for reducing image file size can be applied to reduce the video data rate. Reducing the video file size can be achieved by reducing the data rate and/or reducing the length of the video. The following discussion on file size optimization assumes that the length of the video is fixed. In this situation, reducing file size also means reducing the average data rate.

- **Lower the frame size of the video.**
  For an uncompressed video, reducing its width and height to half of the original will reduce the file size to a quarter of the original. However, video files are often compressed and for a compressed video, the resulting file size may not be strictly a quarter of the original. Nevertheless, lowering the frame size is an effective way to reduce the video file size. Note that you may not be able to control the frame size of a video footage captured by a video camera because the frame size is often dictated by the file format that the camera supports. However, you can reduce the frame size of a video in a video editing program by exporting the video to a different file format.

---

[2] Mark Sullivan. "4G Wireless Speed Tests: Which Is Really the Fastest? AT&T, Sprint, T-Mobile, and Verizon: PCWorld's exclusive performance tests reveal which 4G network delivers the fastest data speeds." *PCWorld.* March 13, 2011. URL: http://www.pcworld.com/printable/article/id,221931/printable.html

- **Lower the frame rate of the video.**

  Reducing the frame rate of a video means lowering the number of frames per second. Thus, the total number of frames in the video is decreased resulting in a smaller file size. In general, the frame rate is proportional to the file size. That is, reducing the frame rate to half will reduce the file size to half of the original. The digital video footage captured by a video camera often has a specific file format, which dictates the frame rate. However, in the video editing program, you can export your final video to a different file format using a lower frame rate.

    Lowering the frame rate affects the smoothness of fast-action content more than it affects talking-head-type videos. To lower the frame rate of a video that is originally shot at 30 fps, you can start at 15 fps and lower the frame rate as much as possible without making the video too choppy. Sometimes, the talking-head-type videos may work fine at a frame rate of as low as 8 or 10 fps.

- **For QuickTime movies, choose a video compressor that supports higher compression.**

  Sorenson Video 3 and H.264 for QuickTime usually give good compression with optimal picture quality. QuickTime Animation and PlanarRGB compressors are good for computer-generated animation, but the resulting file is less compressed.

- **Lower the picture quality of the video.**

  Some compressors let you set the picture quality. The lower the picture quality, the lower the data rate. Some, such as Sorenson (Figure 11), also let you set a limit on data rate. Lowering the data rate sacrifices the video quality. You will need to experiment with the settings and judge whether the resulting quality meets the intended use of the final video.

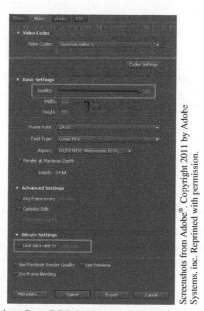

Figure 11 Adobe Premiere Pro CS5.5's Export Movie dialog box with a Sorenson Video 3 compressor chosen.

    For example, two QuickTime movies may be compressed with the same compressor, H.264, but one has the picture quality set to 100% and the other is set to 70%. The file size of the 70% quality movie may be about half that of the 100% one, but there is not much perceivable image degradation.

- **Lower the color depth, if appropriate.**
  This is a least-used strategy because:
  - Most digital video standards (DV, HDV, DVD) have specifications of color space.
  - Live videos usually need 24-bit color to look good. They may not work well with 8-bit color.
  - Some compressors support 24-bit color only.

  However, reducing color depth may work well for some computer-generated graphics or presentations that contain less than 256 colors. A compressor that supports 8-bit color is QuickTime Graphics.
- **Lower the sampling rate, bit depth, and number of channels of the audio.**
  This is another seldom-used strategy because:
  - Lowering the quality of the audio generally has much less impact on the file size than lowering the image quality, frame size, and frame rate of the video. For example, in the previous file size calculation, we see that the audio takes up less than 200 KB per second. The video portion for an HDV 1080i or 1080p takes up 25 Mbps (megabits per second) (Table 4), or about 3 MB per second, which is about 15 times the rate of the audio portion. This means that even if you eliminate the whole audio, only 1/16th of the file size would be saved.
  - Many digital video standards (such as DV, HDV, DVD, Blu-ray) have specifications for the audio sampling rate and bit depth to conform to.

    If you really need to reduce the file size as much as possible (even by lowering the quality of the audio), here are some general rules. The settings for a CD-quality audio are: 44,100-Hz sampling rate, 16 bit, stereo (two channels). If the content of the audio is speech, then a 22,050-Hz sampling rate should be acceptable. If the target audience will be playing the video with low-end speakers, then changing the audio to mono (i.e., reducing the number of channels to one) may be acceptable.

8 GENERAL CONCEPTS OF VIDEO FILE COMPRESSION METHODS

A compressed file must be decompressed before it can be used in normal applications. Think of compressing a file like packing a suitcase.

- Packing your clothes neatly in a suitcase makes it more compact to transport, but it takes time to pack.
- The clothes will need to be unpacked or even ironed before you wear them.
- How the clothes are unpacked often depends on how they were originally packed.

Similarly, it takes time to compress a video file. In addition, a compressed video file must be decompressed before it is played. Compression and decompression always go together as a pair. The term *codec* comes from abridging *c*ompressor/*de*compressor.

The general idea behind the file compression method is to represent the same content by using less data. Some methods involve discarding original data (lossy compression), whereas others preserve the original data (lossless compression).

Many codecs adopt more than one type of method. In general, you do not encounter the name of these compression methods directly in video editing programs. Instead, you are provided with a list of available codecs from which to choose when you export the final video sequence. The following description of the common compression strategies intends to help you make an educated decision in choosing a codec by understanding what the different types of compression methods do to the file and correlating them to the common codec names.

8.1 Spatial Compression

The general goal of **spatial compression** is to compact *individual frames*. This means that the pixel information of each frame is compressed independently from the content of other frames.

Some digital image compression algorithms, such as run-length encoding (RLE) and JPEG compression, are used. Codecs that use spatial compression and RLE are QuickTime Animation, QuickTime PlanarRGB, and Microsoft RLE. RLE works well for video with large areas of solid colors, such as most cartoon animation.

8.2 Temporal Compression

In a typical video sequence, the changes from frame to frame are often very small. **Temporal compression** exploits the repetitious nature of the image content *over time* and the possibility of predicting one frame from the other.

Instead of describing the pixel information of *every* frame, temporal compression only does so in *selected* frames. These frames generally are referred to as **keyframes**. For all other frames, only the *difference* from the previous keyframes is described. If the change between the current frame and the previous keyframe is small, the file size requirement for storing the difference will be smaller than storing the whole frame.

Temporal compression works well for video that contains continuous motion (i.e., the changes from frame to frame are small.) Videos with frequent flickering and scene changes may not be compressed well. Many codecs use temporal compression; for example, Sorenson Video and H.264 for QuickTime.

8.3 Lossless and Lossy Compression

Lossless compression preserves the original data. One of the strategies to do so is to exploit the pattern and repetition of the data, such as with the run-length encoding (RLE) method. Examples of lossless codecs are QuickTime Animation and PlanarRGB—set at the maximum quality setting.

Lossy compression discards or alters some of the original data. The discarded data cannot be recovered and thus the video quality will be lowered. However, the algorithms often take human perception into account when deciding which data will be discarded, so the video will maintain its perceptual quality as much as possible.

Usually, lossy compression results in a much smaller file size than lossless compression. In addition, lowering the quality setting for the lossy compressor lowers the data rate by discarding more original data.

RUN-LENGTH ENCODING (RLE)

RLE compacts a file by replacing a sequence of the same repeated value by one instance of the value followed by the number of times it is repeated. For example, imagine that the color blue is represented in 8 bits as 00001010. If there is a section of sky in a digital image where blue is repeated for 100 pixels, then without any compression, this section would require 800 bits. With RLE, we could encode this section as one instance of blue—00001010—followed by the number 100 in binary (1100100). Instead of 800 bits, we've now used 16 bits—16 digits for 00001010 and 1100100.

8.4 Symmetrical and Asymmetrical Compression

A *symmetrical codec* requires about the same amount of time and processing to compress as to decompress a video. In contrast, the amount of time and the complexity required to compress and decompress are significantly different in *asymmetrical codecs.*

Fast decompression is preferable for video, because the playback will require less wait time. In fact, many codecs fall into the asymmetrical category because it takes much longer to compress a video than to decompress.

The implication of this type of compression pertains to your time management during production. You may choose a fast compression during a time crunch or a fast preview of the work-in-progress video sequence. When you are ready to export the final video, you will need to plan for a much longer time for compression that uses a more efficient codec. For example, the QuickTime Animation codec compresses faster than Sorenson Video. But the video file using the QuickTime Animation codec is generally a lot larger than a file using the Sorenson Video codec.

9 MPEG COMPRESSION

MPEG stands for *Moving Pictures Experts Group*. This committee derives standards for encoding video. The MPEG file format allows high compression. There are several variations of MPEG: MPEG-1, MPEG-2, and MPEG-4.

WHAT HAPPENED TO MPEG-3?

Do not confuse MPEG-3 with MP3. MP3 uses the MPEG-1 audio layer-3 encoding format. MPEG-3 does *not* mean the MP3 audio format.

MPEG-3 was intended as an extension of MPEG-2 to accommodate the standard for HDTV (high-definition television). However, the HDTV specification was then merged into the MPEG-2 standard and the task for deriving the MPEG-3 standard was ended.

9.1 MPEG-1

MPEG-1 provides video quality comparable to VHS tapes and supports frame sizes up to 352×240 pixels. It is also the file format for VideoCD (VCD), which was popular before DVDs became more widespread. Before MPEG-4, it was used for video intended for the Web and CD-ROM playback.

9.2 MPEG-2

MPEG-2 supports the DVD-video, Blu-ray, HDTV, and high-definition video standards. Without going into the details of the specifications of the standard, what this means to digital video production is:

- If your final video is intended for DVD-video, you will need to export the final video into DVD MPEG-2 format. There are different variants of MPEG-2, but only the ones that conform to the DVD specifications can be used for DVD-video.

Fundamentals of Digital Video

Most digital video editing programs provide template settings for DVD export, so you do not need to memorize all of the specification details in order to export a correct MPEG-2 for DVD-video.

- If your final video is intended for Blu-ray format, you will need to export the final video into Blu-ray's MPEG-2 format.

This section intends to introduce a very basic and general explanation of MPEG compression, so you will understand the key parameters that you see in digital video editing programs when exporting your video to DVD MPEG format.

A detailed description of the MPEG standards and MPEG compression algorithms is presented in the CS Module.

How Compression Works

In a typical video sequence, neighboring frames often have a great deal of similarity. This means that there is *temporal redundancy*. MPEG compression exploits the temporal redundancy by looking for motion differences from one frame to the next in order to reduce file size. The technique it uses is called *motion compensation*. The basic idea of the steps used in motion compensation is as follows:

1. An image from the video is read as a reference frame, and then the next image is read.
2. The image of this current or target frame is compared one block of pixels at a time with the reference image. There are two possibilities:
   - If the pixels of the two blocks at the same location in the frame are identical, then there will be no need to encode the pixel information of the current block. An instruction will be included to tell the decoder to use the block from the reference image. This will save more storage size than encoding the whole block.
   - If the two blocks are not identical, then it will search the reference image at different locations for a match. A match may or may not be found.
     - If no match is found, then it will encode that block fully. In this case, there is no saving in file size.
     - However, if a match is found, then the data of the block from the reference image plus the displacement information of the block will be encoded. The displacement information of the current block is called a *motion vector*. It has a two-dimensional value, normally represented by a horizontal component and a vertical component. It tells the decoder exactly where in the reference image to get the data of the pixel block.

The example in Figure 12a represents a reference image and Figure 12b its subsequent frame. In comparing Figure 12b with Figure 12a, some pixel blocks in Figure 12b can be found in Figure 12a; for example, the blocks highlighted in blue in Figure 12f. However, some pixel blocks, such as those highlighted in yellow, cannot be found in Figure 12a.

Figures 13a and 13b show frames 1 and 2 of the previous example. The shaded block with the blue outline in frame 2 (Figure 13b) has a match in the reference frame (frame 1). The motion vector, depicted by a blue line connecting the two blocks in Figure 13c, provides the displacement information of the pixel block.

The example in Figure 12 is a very simple situation where all of the objects in the scene are flat and static. In a typical video, the movement of the subjects is much more complex. The subjects move and rotate in three dimensions, and the movement is not limited to a flat plane parallel to the camera. In addition, the lighting condition may change and the same subject may look differently in the next frame. Identical matches are rarely obtained. Instead, the closest matches are usually what the encoder will find.

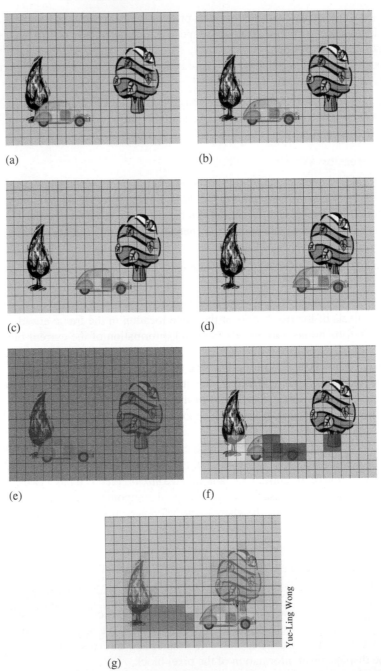

Figure 12 (a) through (d) The first four frames of a video: (a) Frame 1, being the reference frame or the I-frame. (b) Frame 2, being a B-frame. (c) Frame 3, being a B-frame. (d) Frame 4, being a P-frame. (e) through (g) Areas highlighted in red are original pixel information and areas highlighted in blue are from the previous I-frame. Areas highlighted in cyan are from the previous I-frame at the same location, and those highlighted in yellow are from the next P-frame. ▄▟ This image can be found on the insert.

Note: Not all the blocks are labeled for their encoding method; only some are highlighted to illustrate the points.

(a)

(b)

(c)

Yue-Ling Wong

Figure 13 (a) Frame 1 of the example in Figure 12, where the block outlined in blue matches the shaded block outlined in blue in (b). (b) Frame 2 of the same example, where the shaded block with the blue outline is the block under motion search. (c) The location difference is depicted by a blue line—the motion vector.

The color difference between the closest match from the reference frame and the actual pixel block of the current frame will be calculated. If the bits required to store the difference are fewer than encoding the actual pixel block, then the difference and the motion vector will be encoded. Otherwise, the actual pixel block will be encoded.

Group of Pictures (GOP)

Recall that motion compensation is performed by comparing a frame with a reference frame. But how are reference frames chosen? To answer this question, we first need to introduce an important concept in MPEG-1 and MPEG-2: the *group of pictures (GOP)*, which defines the grouping structure of different frame types.

There are three frame types in terms of the information used for encoding the frame: I-frames, P-frames, and B-frames. A GOP structure in an MPEG movie contains one I-frame. It also often consists of a combination of multiple P- and B-frames. A typical MPEG consists of a repeating GOP structure.

I-frames stands for *intraframes*. An I-frame is encoded using only the information within that frame. It is called *intracoding*. In other words, I-frames use spatial compression but no temporal compression.

The encoding of an I-frame is very similar to JPEG compression. Artifacts similar to the artifacts in JPEG images can be seen in MPEG videos (Figure 14).

How does the encoder determine whether it is a match? The basic idea is to measure the differences (color value, pixel by pixel) between the block in the reference frame and the block in the current frame. The one with the minimum difference will be the closest match.

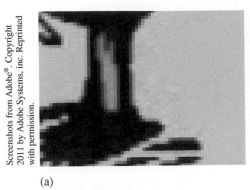
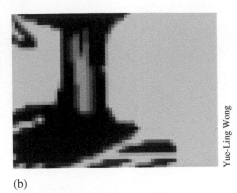

(a)   (b)

Yue-Ling Wong

Figure 14 (a) MPEG artifact, discernible at the intersect area of dark and light colors. (b) The original image before MPEG compression. ▄▄ This image can be found on the insert.

A GOP starts with an I-frame; there is only one I-frame in a GOP. The number of frames, including the I-frame, in a GOP is specified by the parameter *N* of the GOP. The value of *N* for DVD-compliant MPEG-2 is 15. HDV also supports $N = 15$. Because the I-frame is encoded using spatial compression without temporal compression, it is the least-compressed frame type among the three types of frames.

P-frames stands for *predicted frames*. A P-frame is encoded by using the previous I- or P-frame as the reference frame. It is possible that a pixel block in a P-frame will use intra-coding when a match to the reference is not found or when the intracoding will use fewer bits than using the match.

B-frames are the frames between the I- and P-frame, the P- and P-frame, and the P- and next GOP's I-frame. B-frames stands for *bidirectional frames*, which means a B-frame is encoded by using the previous and subsequent I- and/or P-frame as the reference frames.

The parameter *M* of the GOP specifies the number of these frames between the non-B-frames plus one. For DVD-compliant MPEG-2, the *N* and *M* parameters for the GOP are 15 and 3, respectively. In other words, the frames in a GOP are structured as

$$I\ B\ B\ P\ B\ B\ P\ B\ B\ P\ B\ B\ P\ B\ B$$

In this GOP, the first two B-frames are encoded using the previous I-frame and the subsequent P-frame as the reference frames.

The example in Figure 12 is based on this GOP structure. This means that:

- Frame 1 in the example in Figure 12a is the I-frame. The whole frame is intracoded (Figure 12e).
- Frame 4 (Figure 12d) is the first P-frame in the GOP.
- Frames 2 (Figure 12b) and 3 (Figure 12c) are B-frames.

Some blocks in frame 4 are intracoded (highlighted in red in the color insert of Figure 12g). Some blocks (highlighted in blue in the color insert of Figure 12f) in frame 2 (a B-frame) use the I-frame (frame 1) as the reference frame. However, part of a tree trunk in frame 2 is only available in the subsequent P-frame (frame 4), and those blocks (highlighted in yellow) use frame 4 as the reference frame for the tree trunk's pixel information.

You may encounter the *N* and *M* settings for the GOP when you export your video to MPEG-2. Some video editing programs hide the GOP settings from you. Some, such as Adobe Premiere Pro, let you check out or even change the *N* and *M* settings of the GOP when you export an MPEG-2 (Figure 15).

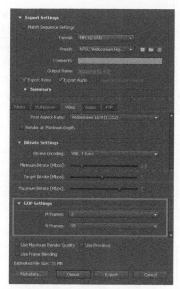

Figure 15 Adobe Premiere Pro CS5.5's DVD MPEG-2 Movie Export window with the red rectangle highlighting the GOP's *M* and *N* parameters.

Consequences of Configurations of GOP Structure

There are at least two consequences of using GOP structure in video; one pertains to the file size and the other to the video editing.

For file size, consider the following:
- An MPEG-2 movie consists of a repeating GOP structure.
- Each GOP contains one I-frame.
- I-frames are the least compressed among the three types of frames, and thus take up more storage space.

What this means to the MPEG-2 file size is that the shorter the GOP (i.e., lower value of N), the more I-frames a video will have. This, in turn, means that the overall file size is larger with a smaller value of N.

For video editing, consider the following:
- The information for a P-frame *depends* on the information of its previous I-frame.
- A B-frame *depends* on the information of its previous and subsequent I- or P-frames.

Because of this dependency, frame-accurate editing for MPEG-2 is more complex than in non-GOP types of videos such as standard-definition DV that uses the DV25 format. Editing MPEG-2 has been difficult because any alteration made on the frame sequence requires decompression and recompression (lossy, and could be slow). However, digital video editing application programs now are designed to allow MPEG editing to work seamlessly.

9.3 MPEG-4

MPEG-4 is the newer standard in the MPEG family. It differs from MPEG-1 and MPEG-2 in the coding approach and the range of the target data rate. The new coding approach uses *media objects*. For example, if the car and the two trees from the scene in Figure 12 are each a media object, then even if the car is blocking part of a tree trunk in one scene, as in Figure 12a, the tree trunk information is still available. This approach allows better motion prediction. As you see in Figure 16d, it is easier to locate an exact match for the pixel block for the back of the car than with traditional frame-based coding (Figure 16e) in MPEG-1 and MPEG-2. The object-based coding also supports content-based manipulation of the scene and thus user interaction with the media objects.

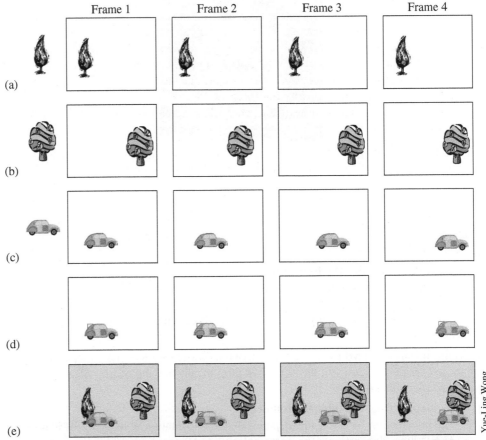

Figure 16 (a) through (c) The rows illustrate the concepts of how elements would be treated as media objects. (d) Same as row (c) but with an outline of a pixel block at the back of the car. (e) A whole frame in traditional frame-based coding; a pixel block at the back of the car is outlined.

Each object in a scene, however, does not have to be separated into a media object in order to produce an MPEG-4 video. A conventional frame-based video—from a digital camcorder—can be converted to MPEG-4 format. In this case, the whole frame, as a rectangular bitmap image, is treated as an object—a degenerated case.

The data rate of the MPEG-4 standard covers a wide range. The low end of the range targets the mobile applications, such as cell phones, that MPEG-1 and MPEG-2 standards do not support. The high end supports the video quality for high-definition television

(HDTV). MPEG-4 is also a video file format supported by HTML5 and many handheld and portable game devices, such as Sony Playstation Portable (PSP).

10 STREAMING VIDEO AND PROGRESSIVE DOWNLOAD

There are two modes of video playback (i.e., two ways of playing videos):

1. **Play from the local storage of the user's device.**
   In this mode of playback, an entire clip needs to be already in the local storage of the user's device before it can be played. The file can be on a hard drive, a USB drive, or an optical disc (such as CD, DVD, and Blu-ray). If the video needs to be obtained from a Web site or any remote network site, then the entire file needs to be downloaded before it can start playing. All video file types support this mode of playback.

2. **Play over a network (typically the Internet).**
   In this mode, the video will be displayed while it is being downloaded. The video file does not have to be downloaded in its entirety before it can be played. Streaming video and progressive download fall into this mode of video playback. Examples of this mode of video playback include Amazon Instant Video, YouTube videos, and Netflix's online subscription.

The common file formats of *streaming video* on the Web are: Adobe Flash Video, Streaming QuickTime, Real Networks' RealVideo, and Windows Media Video (WMV). Streaming video files can also be played from disc. However, in order to stream the video over the Internet, it requires a streaming server, which is a computer running the appropriate streaming server program. For example, streaming Flash videos requires Adobe Flash Media Server, QuickTime requires Apple QuickTime Streaming Server, RealVideo requires RealNetworks Helix Server, and WMV requires Windows Server.

One of the key advantages of streaming is allowing encoding of multiple copies of the same video in different data rates. The streaming server chooses the appropriate one based on the speed of the viewer's connection to minimize disruption of the video playback. For example, Figure 17 shows some choices of different target connection speeds that you can add to a RealVideo file. This technology used by RealVideo and RealAudio is called *SureStream*.

Streaming does not guarantee continuous playback; it still takes time for the data stream to arrive. If the network connection is too slow, there still may be wait time every few frames or longer. When this happens, you usually see a message about "buffering . . ." in your media player.

Unlike other modes of video playback, a true streaming video is never stored on the user's device. If you want to watch the video again, the video will be streamed again.

An alternative method of streaming is *progressive download* or *pseudostreaming*. For example, MP4 and FLV videos can be played back using a mechanism called HTTP Pseudostreaming. This mechanism has been used by YouTube Web site. QuickTime's Fast-Start feature allows playback as soon as enough of the data stream has arrived.

Progressive download does not require a streaming server. The file is transferred to the local storage of the user's device as with non-progressive download. The file usually remains on the user's device after playback, for example, in the Web browser's cache if the video is played in the Web browser. Therefore, after the entire video has been played once, it can be played again from the Web browser's cache on the user's device without having to wait for download again.

A simple way to convert a Quick-Time movie into a Fast-Start movie is to save the Quick-Time movie as a self-contained movie in Quick-Time Pro, a professional version of QuickTime player.

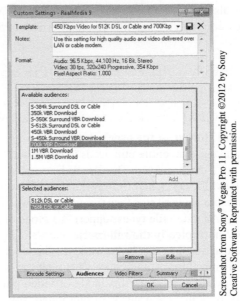

Figure 17 A dialog box showing a list of target connection speeds you can choose from when exporting a video to RealVideo format using Sony Vegas Pro 11.

11 SUMMARY

Video captures our temporal experience of sights and sounds. Conceptually, video captures motion as a sequence of pictures at a constant time interval. Each picture is called a frame. The frame size also is referred to as resolution of the video. It is measured in the pixel dimensions of a frame—its width by its height, expressed in number of pixels. How fast the pictures are captured or how fast the frames are played back is determined by the frame rate, which is measured in frames per second (fps).

The concepts of sampling and quantization applied to still images also apply to the visual component of the video, and those applied to the digital audio also apply to the auditory component.

In many situations, the available choices in digital video settings, such as frame size and frame rate, are influenced by digital video standards, which, in turn, are influenced by the analog television broadcast standards. There are three sets of broadcast standards for analog color televisions: NTSC, PAL, and SECAM. They differ in frame sizes, frame rates, and color spaces.

For an NTSC standard-definition DV frame, the frame size is 720 × 480 pixels. The frame size for a PAL standard DV frame is 720 × 576 pixels. For high-definition digital video, the HDV format, for example, has two frame sizes: 1,280 × 720 pixels and 1,440 × 1,080 pixels.

The frame aspect ratio is the ratio of its width-to-height dimensions. For example, the frame aspect ratio for the standard-format NTSC DV is 4:3, whereas the wide-screen format is 16:9. The frame aspect ratio for high-definition digital video and high-definition television (HDTV) is 16:9.

Some video formats use non-square pixels to make up the frame. The shape of the pixel can be described by an attribute called pixel aspect ratio. For a square pixel, its pixel aspect ratio is equal to 1. A pixel aspect ratio of less than 1 depicts a tall pixel, whereas a pixel aspect ratio of greater than 1 depicts a wide pixel. A video should be displayed on a system with the matching pixel aspect ratio; otherwise, the image will be distorted.

Timecode is used to number frames in a video. The two common formats of timecode used in digital video are drop frame and non-drop frame. No frame is dropped or lost in either timecode. The drop-frame timecode is preferable for the NTSC system to maintain the time accuracy.

Computers display the picture by displaying lines from top to bottom in one pass—progressive scan. Analog television standards for NTSC, PAL, and SECAM display the picture in two passes. For NTSC, the first pass traces the even-numbered lines, and the second pass traces the odd-numbered lines to fill in the alternating gaps left by the first pass. The set of the lines in the same pass (i.e., the set of even lines or odd lines) is called a field. This display method of using two alternating fields is called interlaced scan.

Digital television (DTV) refers to television signals that are broadcast or transmitted digitally. At the time of this writing, in the United States, there are 18 DTV formats developed by the Advanced Television Systems Committee, Inc. (ATSC). The 18 formats include 12 formats for standard-definition television (SDTV) and 6 for high-definition television (HDTV). There are two frame aspect ratios for the SDTV format—4:3 and 16:9—whereas the frame aspect ratio of all six HDTV formats is 16:9. HDTV has higher resolution than the traditional analog TV and SDTV. It uses the MPEG-2 format.

The data rate refers to the amount of video data to be processed per second. The average data rate of a video is calculated by dividing the file size by the total length of the video in seconds. It provides a measure for predicting the smoothness of the video playback on devices. If a video's data rate is too high for a playback device to handle, the playback of the video will be choppy. Lowering the video data rate can be achieved by reducing the video file size. The general strategies to reduce video file size include: (1) lowering the frame size of the video, (2) lowering the frame rate of the video, and (3) using a compressor that allows higher compression.

MPEG stands for Moving Pictures Experts Group. It is a file format that allows high compression. There are several variations of MPEG: MPEG-1, MPEG-2, and MPEG-4. MPEG-1 supports the VideoCD format. MPEG-2 supports the DVD-video, Blu-ray, high-definition video, and HDTV standards. MPEG-4 is the newer standard of the MPEG family. It differs from MPEG-1 and MPEG-2 in the coding approach and the range of target data rate. MPEG-4's low-end range of data rate targets the mobile applications, such as cell phones, that MPEG-1 and MPEG-2 standards do not support. The high-end supports the video quality for HDTV and high-definition video.

There are two modes of video playback: play from the local storage of the user's device and play over a network. When playing from the user's device, an entire clip needs to be already on the device before it can be played. In playing over the network, the video will be displayed as the data stream arrives. In other words, a video file does not have to be downloaded in its entirety before it can be played. Streaming video and progressive download or pseudostreaming fall into this mode of video playback. True streaming requires a streaming server but progressive download does not.

TERMS

1080i	group of pictures	PAL
1080p	(GOP)	P-frames
4:1:1	HDV	pixel aspect ratio
4:2:0	high-definition television	predicted frames
4:2:2	(HDTV)	progressive download
4:4:4	I-frames	progressive scan
720p	interlaced scan	pseudostreaming
Advanced Television	intracoding	resolution
Systems Committee,	intraframes	safe action area
Inc. (ATSC)	keyframes	safe title area
asymmetrical	lossless compression	SECAM
codecs	lossy compression	SMPTE
B-frames	lower field	spatial compression
bidirectional frames	luminance	standard-definition digital
chroma subsampling	M	video
chrominance	media objects	standard-definition
codec	motion compensation	television (SDTV)
data rate	motion vector	streaming video
DV compression	Moving Pictures Experts	SureStream
DV25	Group	symmetrical codec
DVCPRO HD	MPEG	temporal compression
field	MPEG-1	temporal redundancy
frame	MPEG-2	timecode
frame aspect ratio	MPEG-4	upper field
frame rate	N	video frame size
frame size	NTSC	YIQ
frames per second (fps)	overscan	YUV

LEARNING AIDS

The following learning aids can be found at the text's companion Web site.

Video display: Interlaced Scan versus Progressive Scan

An interactive animation that illustrates two-pass scanning in interlaced scan and one-pass scanning in progressive scan.

Upper Field and Lower Field

An interactive demo shows the upper field and the lower field of a video frame.

Fast-Action Digital Video Showing the Interlace Artifact

A soccer practice video clip of Figure 1 shows the comb-like interlace artifact.

Video Recording: Interlaced Mode versus Progressive Mode

An interactive animation that illustrates how the interlace artifact may be produced in fast-action videos.

Pixel Aspect Ratio

An interactive demo shows you the effect of an incorrect pixel aspect ratio on an image.

REVIEW QUESTIONS

When applicable, please choose all correct answers.

1. Which of the following is the television broadcast standard for the United States and Japan?

    A. NTSC
    B. PAL
    C. SECAM

2. Which of the following is the television broadcast standard for most of the Asian countries?

    A. NTSC
    B. PAL
    C. SECAM

3. Which of the following is the most common color model for video?

    A. RGB
    B. HSV
    C. CIE XYZ
    D. luminance-chrominance

4. In the YUV color model, the Y-component is _____, the U-component is _____, and the V-component is _____.

    A. luminance; luminance; chrominance
    B. luminance; chrominance; luminance
    C. luminance; chrominance; chrominance
    D. chrominance; chrominance; luminance
    E. chrominance; luminance; luminance

5. The frame rate for the NTSC system is _____ fps.

    A. 24
    B. 25
    C. 28.9
    D. 29.97
    E. 30

6. The frame rate for the PAL system is _____ fps.

    A. 24
    B. 25
    C. 28.9
    D. 29.97
    E. 30

7. The frame rate for motion-picture film is _____ fps.

    A. 24
    B. 25
    C. 28.9
    D. 29.97
    E. 30

8. Interlaced scan displays the frame by scanning the lines of a frame _____.

   A. in one pass from top to bottom
   B. in two passes: even-numbered lines in one pass and odd-numbered lines in the second

9. Progressive scan displays the frame by scanning the lines of a frame _____.

   A. in one pass from top to bottom
   B. in two passes: even-numbered lines in one pass and odd-numbered lines in the second

10. The comb-like artifact in a digital video, as shown in Figure 18, occurs in the _____ video.

Figure 18 A digital video frame showing comb-like artifacts.

   A. interlaced
   B. progressive
   C. both A and B

11. **True/False:** There is no sampling and quantization involved in capturing motion in digital video.

12. The frame size of a video refers to the video's _____.

   A. aspect ratio
   B. pixel aspect ratio
   C. resolution
   D. ppi

13. **True/False:** The pixel per inch (ppi) is an important attribute for video resolution and should be set correctly when working with digital video in video editing programs.

14. Pixel aspect ratio means _____.

   A. the ratio of a frame's width (in pixels) to its height (in pixels)
   B. the ratio of a frame's height (in pixels) to its width (in pixels)
   C. the ratio of a pixel's width to its height
   D. the ratio of a pixel's height to its width

15. The pixel aspect ratio of a wide-screen-format, standard-definition video is _____.

A. 4:3
B. 16:9
C. 1.0
D. 0.9
E. 1.2

16. The pixel aspect ratio of a standard-format, standard-definition video is _____.

A. 4:3
B. 16:9
C. 1.0
D. 0.9
E. 1.2

17. The frame aspect ratio of a wide-screen-format, standard-definition video is _____.

A. 4:3
B. 16:9
C. 1.0
D. 0.9
E. 1.2

18. The frame aspect ratio of a standard-format, standard-definition video is _____.

A. 4:3
B. 16:9
C. 1.0
D. 0.9
E. 1.2

19. The frame aspect ratio of a high-definition video is _____.

A. 4:3
B. 16:9
C. 1.0
D. 0.9
E. 1.2

20. If a frame with a pixel aspect ratio of 1.2 is displayed on a device using a pixel aspect ratio of 1.0, the image will be _____.

A. stretched horizontally
B. stretched vertically
C. cropped at the left and right edges
D. cropped at the top and bottom
E. displayed correctly

21. **True/False:** The timecode representing the 35th frame is either 00:00:00:35 or 00;00;00;35.

22. **True/False:** The drop-frame timecode drops or discards frames to preserve the time accuracy of a video.

23. Which of the following is the drop-frame timecode format?

    A. 00:00:00:00
    B. 00;00;00;00
    C. 00,00,00,00
    D. 00.00.00.00

24. Which timecode format is preferable for the NTSC system?

    A. Drop frame
    B. Non-drop frame

25. Chroma subsampling reduces the storage of pixel information by assigning fewer bits to store the _____ components.

    A. RGB
    B. luminance
    C. chrominance

26. The format of chroma subsampling is designated with three numbers separated by colons (for example, 4:2:2) to represent _____.

    A. the ratio of red:green:blue
    B. the ratio of the luminance to the two chrominance components
    C. the ratio of the number of three different types of pixels
    D. hours:minutes:seconds
    E. the ratio of the number of three different types of frames in a GOP

27. **True/False:** The signals of digital television are broadcast or transmitted digitally.

28. **True/False:** The frame aspect ratio of all six HDTV formats is 16:9.

29. HDTV is in _____ format.

    A. MPEG-1
    B. MPEG-2
    C. MPEG-3
    D. MPEG-4
    E. QuickTime
    F. AVI

30. The frame size for NTSC standard-definition DV is _____ pixels, and _____ pixels for the PAL system.

    A. 720 × 480; 720 × 480
    B. 720 × 576; 720 × 576
    C. 720 × 480; 720 × 576
    D. 720 × 576; 720 × 480

31. The numbers 720 and 1080 in the high-definition video picture format notations such as 720/30p and 1080/60i designate the _____.

A. data rate of the video
B. width (in pixels) of the frame size
C. height (in pixels) of the frame size
D. ppi of the video
E. none of the above; they are model numbers of different companies

32. The letters "p" and "i" in the high-definition video picture format notations such as 720/30p and 1080/60i stand for _____ and _____, respectively.

A. pixels; inches
B. professional; intermediate
C. progressive; interlaced
D. pixels per inch; inches per pixel

33. **True/False:** A very long video, even with low data rate, can have a large file size.

34. Suppose you are on broadband connection with a speed of 6 Mbps. For a 1-minute video file with a file size of 20 MB, its playback through pseudostreaming on the Web very likely will be _____.

A. smooth
B. choppy

35. Suppose you are on broadband connection with a speed of 6 Mbps. For a 5-second video file with a file size of 20 MB, its playback through pseudostreaming on the Web very likely will be _____.

A. smooth
B. choppy

36. Suppose your target audience uses a broadband connection with a speed of 6 Mbps. What is the maximum file size for your 30-second video to have a smooth playback using pseudostreaming on the Web? Show your calculations.

37. Which of the following provides a measure for predicting the smoothness of video playback? If the value of that property is too high for the playback device to handle, the playback of the video will be choppy.

A. file size
B. frame size
C. frame rate
D. frame aspect ratio
E. pixel aspect ratio
F. data rate

38. Name several strategies to reduce the file size of a video.

39. What does the term *codec* stand for?

40. _____ compression refers to the type of compression method that aims at compacting individual frames.

A. Asymmetric
B. Lossless
C. Lossy
D. Spatial
E. Temporal

41. _____ compression refers to the type of compression method that exploits the similarity of the subsequent frame content.

A. Asymmetric
B. Lossless
C. Lossy
D. Spatial
E. Temporal

42. _____ compression refers to the type of compression method that preserves the original data.

A. Asymmetric
B. Lossless
C. Lossy
D. Spatial
E. Temporal

43. _____ compression refers to the type of compression method that discards or alters some of the original data.

A. Asymmetric
B. Lossless
C. Lossy
D. Spatial
E. Temporal

44. _____ compression refers to the type of compression method in which the amount of time and the complexity required to compress and decompress are significantly different.

A. Asymmetric
B. Lossless
C. Lossy
D. Spatial
E. Temporal

45. Which of the following compression methods achieves higher compression for videos without much motion difference, such as for talking heads?

A. Spatial compression
B. Temporal compression
C. Lossless compression
D. Asymmetric compression

46. Which of the following types of video can be compressed the most with temporal compression?

A. Fast action
B. Slow, continuous motion

47. Which of the following compression methods works best with large areas of solid color, such as in a cartoon animation?

A. QuickTime Animation
B. MPEG-1
C. MPEG-2

48. **True/False:** The MP3 audio is an MPEG-3.

49. Which of the following support the DVD-video, high-definition video, and HDTV standards?

A. MPEG-1
B. MPEG-2
C. MPEG-3
D. MPEG-4

50. Which of the following also targets mobile applications, such as cell phones?

A. MPEG-1
B. MPEG-2
C. MPEG-3
D. MPEG-4

51. **True/False:** A typical MPEG-2 consists of a repeating GOP structure.

52. Motion compensation is a key technique in _____ compression.

A. asymmetric
B. lossless
C. lossy
D. spatial
E. temporal

53. The _____ is encoded using only the information within that frame.

A. B-frame
B. I-frame
C. P-frame

54. The _____ is encoded using only the previous I- or P-frame as the reference frame.

A. B-frame
B. I-frame
C. P-frame

55. The _____ is encoded using the previous and subsequent I- and/or P-frames as the reference frames.

A. B-frame
B. I-frame
C. P-frame

56. The _____ is the least compressed.

   A. B-frame
   B. I-frame
   C. P-frame
   D. none of the above; all are compressed at the same level

57. The *M* parameter of the GOP refers to _____.

   A. the number of B-frames in a GOP
   B. the number of I-frames in a GOP
   C. the number of P-frames in a GOP
   D. the total number of frames in a GOP
   E. one plus the number of frames between the non-B-frames

58. The *N* parameter of the GOP refers to _____.

   A. the number of B-frames in a GOP
   B. the number of I-frames in a GOP
   C. the number of P-frames in a GOP
   D. the total number of frames in a GOP
   E. one plus the number of frames between the non-B-frames

59. True/False: There is only one I-frame in a GOP structure.

60. True/False: There is only one I-frame in an MPEG video.

61. Explain why, in general, the longer GOP structure allows more file size compression. (*Hint*: Consider the number of I-frames in a GOP structure and the different levels of compression for different frame types.)

62. True/False: Progressive download requires a streaming server.

63. True/False: True streaming requires a streaming server.

64. True/False: Progressive download and pseudostreaming allow the video to start playing as soon as enough of the video data has arrived.

65. True/False: For streaming video, the file usually remains on the user's device after playback, for example, in the Web browser's cache.

66. True/False: In progressive download, the file usually remains on the user's device after playback, for example, in the Web browser's cache.

67. "After the entire video has been played once in a Web browser, it can be replayed without having to wait for download again."
   Which of the following modes of video playback match(es) this description?

   A. True streaming
   B. Progressive download or pseudo-streaming
   C. None of the above

Introduction to HTML

TABLE OF CONTENTS

Courtesy of Yue-Ling Wong

Summary   Terms   Learning Aids   Review Questions

From Chapter 14 of *Digital Media Primer and Digital Audio, Video, Imaging and Multimedia Programming*, Second Edition. Yue-Ling Wong. Copyright © 2013 by Pearson Education, Inc. All rights reserved.

KEY CONCEPTS
- HTML documents
- XHTML
- Tags and attributes
- Nested tags
- Links
- Relative and absolute paths

GENERAL LEARNING OBJECTIVES

In this chapter, you will learn

- The basic structure for an HTML document.
- How to use the HTML tags: <p>, <br>, <h1>-<h6>, <b>, <i>, <strong>, <em>, <a>, <img>, and tags for tables.
- How to construct absolute and relative file paths.
- How to construct and read document-relative file paths in creating links and embedding images on a Web page.

1 WEB PAGES, HTML, AND WEB BROWSERS

In general, the term *Web pages* refers to documents that are written in a language called HTML. *HTML* stands for *Hypertext Markup Language*. An HTML file is a text file. The text file consists of plain text (i.e., the text itself does not have any formatting), so there is no boldface or italics. The tabs and line breaks in the text file do not appear when the document is viewed on a Web browser. However, the text can be marked with special markup codes called *tags*. These markup tags tell the Web browser how to display the page. For example, you will need to add a tag to create a line break on a Web page. Think of the HTML code as the written *instructions* of how the page should look. A *Web browser* is an application that can interpret these instructions and display the document in the format and layout according to the markup tags.

You can create an HTML document using a text editor, such as Notepad in Windows or TextEdit in Mac OS. You also can create an HTML document using a Web page editor, such as Adobe Dreamweaver. No matter which way an HTML document is created or edited, it is still a text file. For instance, if you create a Web page in Dreamweaver, you still can open it with Notepad, and vice versa. The difference between editing an HTML document with a text editor and a Web page editor is that you see only HTML code in a text editor. A Web page editor lets you see both the code and how the page may be displayed in a Web browser while you are editing the page. It also allows you to edit the page visually without having to manually add markup tags.

Before introducing the basics of writing HTML documents, let's first explain some common terms for working with the Web as a medium.

URL

URL stands for ***Uniform Resource Locator***. This is the standard for specifying the address of Web pages and other resources on the World Wide Web. URLs for Web pages have a similar structure that is made up of segments representing standard information. Let's look at the following example to see how an URL is structured.

`http://digitalmedia.wfu.edu/project/index.html`

- **Beginning segment:** `http://`
  This means that the page is located on a Web server. ***http*** stands for ***Hypertext Transfer Protocol***. It refers to the sets of rules that govern the information transfer between the Web server and your computer (referred to as a Web client) that is requesting to view the page.
- **Next segment:** `digitalmedia.wfu.edu`
  This is the domain name of the Web server.
- **Rest of the address:** `/project/index.html`
  This is the file path of the document `index.html`. The file path is the location information of the page on the Web server. In this example, the file name of the page is `index.html`. It is located in a folder called `project`.

XHTML

XHTML stands for ***Extensible Hypertext Markup Language***. It is intended to be a replacement for HTML. It has stricter rules for writing HTML and is almost identical to the HTML 4.01 standard. There are different rules for HTML and XHTML, but most of the tags are the same. The stricter rules enforced in XHTML also are supported—but may not be enforced—in HTML. If you have working experience with HTML, you may have been following these rules all along. These rules will be discussed in Section 2.3, where you will learn how to construct a basic HTML document from scratch.

Unless specified, the term HTML, such as in HTML documents and HTML tags, used in this text refers to both HTML and XHTML in general.

Cascading Style Sheets (CSS)

Style sheets allow you to define styles to display HTML elements. Multiple style definitions can be combined or cascaded into one—thus the term ***cascading style sheets***. Like HTML documents, style sheet files are text files. The styles defined in the files follow specific rules and syntax. CSS is widely used for Web page design and layout.

JavaScript and Dynamic HTML (DHTML)

JavaScript is a scripting language for Web pages. It can be used to add interactivity, generate content on the Web page based on the viewer's choice, validate online forms before submission, and create and track cookies.

  Dynamic HTML (DHTML) itself is not a programming language but a combination of HTML, CSS, and JavaScript. JavaScript can make a Web page more dynamic. When combined with CSS, JavaScript can be used to control properties such as text styles, color, visibility, and positioning of HTML elements dynamically.

HTML5

HTML5 is the newest standard of HTML. At the time of writing, its specifications are still a work in progress. The new features of HTML5 include:

- video and audio tags.
- content-specific tags, such as footer, header, nav, article, section, figure, summary, and aside.

- tags for form elements
- canvas element that allows drawing graphics and displaying images dynamically using JavaScript
- allowing storage and retrieval of data on the user's device using JavaScript

2 BASIC ANATOMY OF AN HTML DOCUMENT

This section explains the basic structure of a HTML document.

2.1 Tags and Attributes

HTML documents are written as text files that do not have formatting. The line breaks in the text file, the font, and the font size used in the text editor to create the text file are ignored when the file is displayed in the Web browser. The formatting or presentation of the text is specified using special markup code (called *tags*). These markup tags tell the Web browser how to format the text when displaying it.

Each HTML tag is surrounded by two angle brackets: < and >. For example, the paragraph tag is <p>. Each tag comes in pairs, for example, <p> and </p>. The first tag, <p>, is the *start tag*. The second tag, </p>, is the *end tag* or *closing tag*. To mark up a block of text as a paragraph, you put the text between the <p> and </p> tags, like this:

```
<p> This is a paragraph.</p>
```

The text placed between the start and end tags is the ***element content***. In this example the element content of this <p> tag is: This is a paragraph. The whole element begins with the start tag and ends with the closing tag. You will learn some common tags and examples of their use later in the chapter.

There are some tags that do not have element content. Examples of these tags are the line break <br> and the image tag <img>. For these tags, you either can add a closing tag (such as </br> and </img>) or end the tag with /> (for example, <br />). Section 3 will introduce the usage of some commonly used HTML tags, including these two.

Attributes

A tag may have attributes. ***Attributes*** of a tag specify properties of the element that is marked up by the tag. For example, the id attribute assigns a name to the element. The following shows the HTML code where an id attribute is added to a <p> tag.

```
<p id="introduction">This is a paragraph.</p>
```

In this example, an id attribute is added inside the <p> tag and assigned with a value of "introduction". id is a useful attribute. You can use JavaScript to refer to the element by its id to control its properties, such as the position and the element content.

There are several rules for adding attributes in XHTML:

- Attributes are added inside the start tag.
- Attributes come in as name-value pairs. The name and the value are separated by an equal sign. In the previous example, the attribute name is id, and its value is "introduction".
- The value must be enclosed with quotation marks.
- The attribute names are lowercase.

2.2 A Bare-Bones Structure of an HTML Document

The very basic, bare-bones structure of an HTML document looks like this:

```
<html>
<head>
<title>This is a title.</title>
</head>
<body>
This is the content of the Web page.
</body>
</html>
```

<html> Tag

The first tag in an HTML document is <html>. This tag tells your browser that this is the start of an HTML document. Its end tag </html> is the last tag of the document. This tag tells your browser that this is the end of the HTML document.

<head> Tag

The text placed between the <head> and </head> is the header information. The header information is not displayed in the browser window. Things that may be placed in the header section include the title element (See the <title> tag below), the function definitions of the JavaScript, links to the source of external JavaScript, and links to external style sheets.

<title> Tag

The text between the <title> tag and </title> tag is the title of your document. The title is displayed on the Window bar of your browser window. In addition, when people bookmark your Web page, this title text is used as the default title stored in their browser's bookmark list.

<body> Tag

The content between the <body> tags is the content of the Web page that will be displayed in the browser.

Nested Tags

Markup elements can be nested in another element (i.e., placed within another element's content). For example, the header and body elements are nested inside the <html>, and the <title> is nested inside the <head> (Figure 1). Also notice the placement of the end tags in this example. This is similar to how parentheses are paired in a mathematical equation.

```
    ┌──►  <html>
    ├─►  <head>
    │      <title>This is a title.</title>
    └─►  </head>
    ┌─►  <body>
    │      This is the content of the Web page.
    └─►  </body>
    └─►  </html>
```

Figure 1 Pairing of markup tags in an HTML document.

2.3 XHTML

An XHTML document has the same basic structure as an HTML document, plus it has a DOCTYPE declaration.

DOCTYPE Declaration

DOCTYPE stands for *document type*. The DOCTYPE declaration uses the <!DOCTYPE> tag. The declaration is placed in the very first line in an HTML document, before the <html> tag. The declaration tells the browser which HTML or XHTML specification the document uses, so that the browser will display the page correctly using the appropriate specification. If the code used in the HTML document does not match the DOCTYPE declared, then some of the elements may not be displayed as expected.

The XHTML 1.0 specifies three document types:[*] Strict, Transitional, and Frameset.

- Strict
  The DOCTYPE declaration for the Strict document type is
  ```
  <!DOCTYPE html PUBLIC "-//W3C//DTD XHTML 1.0 Strict//EN"
  "http://www.w3.org/TR/xhtml1/DTD/xhtml1-strict.dtd">
  ```
- Transitional
  The DOCTYPE declaration for the Transitional document type is
  ```
  <!DOCTYPE html PUBLIC "-//W3C//DTD XHTML 1.0 Transitional//EN"
  "http://www.w3.org/TR/xhtml1/DTD/xhtml1-transitional.dtd">
  ```
  This is currently the most common type of DOCTYPE used in Web pages. The Transitional document type allows some leniency for tags and attributes that are going to be deprecated and replaced by CSS.
- Frameset
  The DOCTYPE declaration for the Frameset document type is
  ```
  <!DOCTYPE html PUBLIC "-//W3C//DTD XHTML 1.0 Frameset//EN"
  "http://www.w3.org/TR/xhtml1/DTD/xhtml1-frameset.dtd">
  ```
  The Frameset document type should be used with documents that are framesets. Frames are not preferable for Web page design and are the least used DOCTYPE for new Web pages.

Basic Document Structure of an XHTML Document

The basic HTML document example that is shown in Figure 1 can be rewritten into an XHTML document using the Transitional document type like this:

```
<!DOCTYPE html PUBLIC "-//W3C//DTD XHTML 1.0 Transitional//EN"
"http://www.w3.org/TR/xhtml1/DTD/xhtml1-transitional.dtd">
<html xmlns="http://www.w3.org/1999/xhtml">
<head>
<title>This is a title.</title>
</head>
<body>
This is the content of the Web page.
</body>
</html>
```

---

[*] http://www.w3.org/TR/xhtml1/.

Except for the code added at the beginning of the document, the basic document structure is the same as that of the HTML document shown in Figure 1.

Differences between the Rules for XHTML and HTML

Here are several main differences between XHTML and HTML coding:

- XHTML elements must always be closed or paired.

    For example, the paragraph <p> tag must have a closing tag </p>. For empty elements, such as <br> or <img> tags, you either can add a closing tag (such as </br> and </img>) or end the tag with /> (for example, <br />).
- XHTML tags and attributes must be in lowercase.
- XHTML elements must be properly nested within each other.

    Figure 2 shows the proper and improper nesting of the <p> and <div> tags.

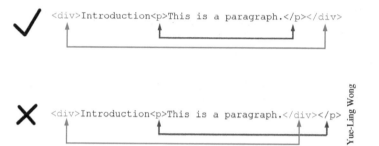

Figure 2 (a) The <div> and <p> tags are properly nested (b) The <div> and <p> tags are not properly nested

- An XHTML document must have one root element (i.e., the topmost element).

    The <html> is the root element of an XHTML document. Elements can have subelements or child elements. Subelements must be in pairs and correctly nested within their parent element. The HTML element must designate the XHTML namespace, like this:

```
<html xmlns="http://www.w3.org/1999/xhtml">
```

    xmlns is the namespace attribute. The value used here is an URL. Although this Web address carries information about the definitions of the XHTML tags, it is not used by the browser to look up information. Its purpose is to give the namespace a unique name.

    When a namespace is defined like this in the start tag of an element, all of its child elements also are associated with the same namespace. Here, the namespace is defined in <html>, which is the root element of the document. Thus, all of the tags in the document are associated with the same namespace.
- There must be a DOCTYPE declaration in the document prior to the root element.

3 COMMON HTML TAGS

This section introduces some common HTML tags.

3.1 Paragraph

The <***p***> tag is used to define paragraphs. For example,

```
<p>This is the first paragraph.</p>
<p>This is the second paragraph.</p>
```

Figure 3 shows how the two paragraphs in this example are displayed in a Web browser. By default, a blank line is automatically inserted before and after a paragraph. Two contiguous paragraphs are separated by one blank line.

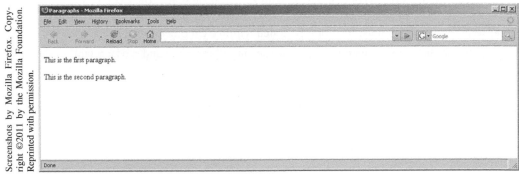

Figure 3 Two paragraphs created using <p> tags.

3.2 Line Break

The <***br***> tag is used to create a line break—to force a new line without starting a new paragraph. Unlike the <p> tag, <br> will not insert a blank line by default. The new line created using the <br> tag keeps the single-line spacing with the rest of the paragraph.

 does not have any element content. To conform to the rule of a closing tag, a closing tag </br> can be added like this:
</br>. However, it commonly is written as: <br />.

Here is an example code using <br />.

```
<p>This is the first paragraph.<br />This is a new line of the
same paragraph.</p>
<p>This is the second paragraph.</p>
```

Figure 4 shows how this example is displayed in a Web browser. The second line "This is a new line of the same paragraph." is forced to a new line using the <br /> tag. Note that this line has single-line spacing with the same paragraph.

Figure 4 Two paragraphs created using <p> tags. The first paragraph uses a <br /> tag to insert a line break.

3.3 Headings

There are several heading tags: *<h1>* through *<h6>*. The number in the heading tag indicates the heading level. For example:

```
<h1>This is a heading 1</h1>
<h2>This is a heading 2</h2>
<h3>This is a heading 3</h3>
<h4>This is a heading 4</h4>
<h5>This is a heading 5</h5>
<h6>This is a heading 6</h6>
```

By default, <h1> has the largest text and <h6> the smallest. Figure 5 shows how these headings are displayed in a Web browser. Note that by default, a blank line is inserted before and after a heading.

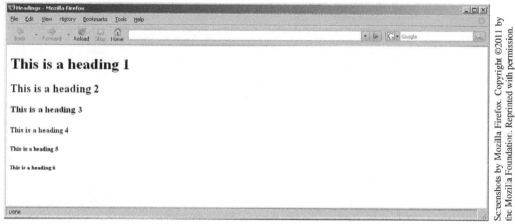

Figure 5 Examples of headings.

3.4 Bold and Italics

The *<b>* or *<strong>* tag can be used to indicate boldfaced text, and the *<i>* or *<em>* tag to indicate italicized text. For example:

<b> and <i> were widely used before CSS was available. Some existing Web pages may still contain these tags.

```
<p>This is normal text.</p>
<p>
<b>This text is bold. </b>
<i>This text is italic.</i>
</p>
<p>
<b><i>This text is bold and italic.</i></b>
</p>
<p>
<i><b>This text is also bold and italic.</b></i>
</p>
```

Using <strong> and <em> tags, the previous code can be rewritten as:

```
<p>This is normal text.</p>
<p>
<strong>This text is bold.</strong>
<em>This text is italic.</em>
</p>
<p>
<strong><em>This text is bold and italic.</em></strong>
</p>
<p>
<em><strong>This text is also bold and italic.</strong></em>
</p>
```

Figure 6 shows how the text looks in a browser. Note that you can nest both <strong> (or <b>) and <em> (or <i>) tags to make text bold and italic. To conform to the XHTML standard, the closing tags need to be placed in the correct order. Think of how the parentheses are closed in mathematical equations.

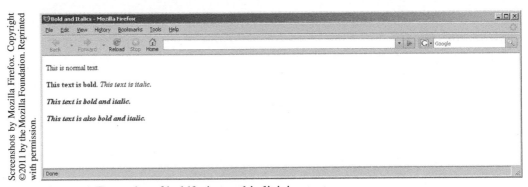

Figure 6 Examples of boldfacing and italicizing text.

The two lines of code here produce the same effect. The <strong> and <em> tags are closed properly in both cases.

```
<strong><em>This text is bold and italic.</em></strong>
<em><strong>This text is bold and italic.</strong></em>
```

The tags in the following statements are not properly closed. These codes may not give errors with current Web browsers and the text may even be displayed correctly as bold and italic. However, future Web browsers may not have such leniency.

```
<p><strong><em>This text is bold and italic.</strong></em></p>
<p><em><strong>This text is also bold and italic.
</em></strong></p>
```

It is worth noting that using these tags to format individual text is not recommended. Instead, you should use cascading style sheets to define text formatting as styles based on the semantics of the element, and then apply the style to the HTML element.

3.5 List

An HTML list displays a list of items marked with bullets, numbers, or even images. There are two types of lists: ordered lists and unordered lists. They are categorized by how the items are marked. Items in an ***ordered list*** are marked with auto numbers. An ***unordered list*** marks items with bullets or images.

The tag for the ordered list is <***ol***>, and the tag for the unordered list is <***ul***>. Each item in the list (regardless of which type) is marked up using the tag <***li***>. For example:

Ordered List:

```
<ol>
    <li>Item A</li>
    <li>Item B</li>
    <li>Item C</li>
</ol>
```

Unordered List:

```
<ul>
    <li>Item A</li>
    <li>Item B</li>
    <li>Item C</li>
</ul>
```

Figure 7 shows how these ordered and unordered lists are displayed in the Web browser.

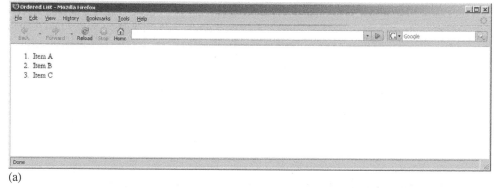

(a)

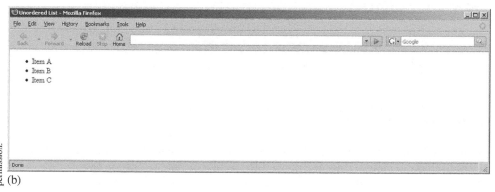

(b)

Figure 7
(a) The items in an ordered list are automatically marked with numbers. (b) The items in an unordered list are marked with bullets.

3.6 Link

The *anchor tag* (denoted by <*a*>) is used to create a link to another document. The attribute `href` is used to specify the address of the document to be linked to. The general syntax to create a link is

```
<a href="url or a file path">Text to be displayed as a clickable link</a>
```

Do not confuse the text content with the value (i.e., the actual URL) for the `href` attribute. The actual URL is not displayed on the Web page in the browser.

The following example creates a link to `http://www.google.com/`. With this code, the Web browser will display the text `Google Web Site` as a clickable link. The URL specified for the `href` attribute `http://www.google.com/`, however, is not displayed on the Web page.

```
<a href="http://www.google.com/">Google Web Site</a>
```

> HTML: Basic HTML Document Structure, Paragraphs, Line Breaks, Lists, Links, Heading, Bold and Italic Text (LAB) Hand-code two HTML documents using basic HTML document structure.

The document to be linked is not limited to an HTML document but can be any file, such as an image, a digital video, an audio, a Microsoft Word document, a PowerPoint file, or an Adobe Acrobat document. If the linked file cannot be opened within the Web browser, the browser will prompt you to download and save the file.

3.7 Image

The <*img*> tag lets you insert an image on a Web page. The attribute `src` (which stands for *source*) is used to specify the location where the image is stored. The general syntax for the <img> tag is:

```
<img src="url or a file path" />
```

The <img> tag does not have any element content. To conform to the rule of a closing tag, a slash is added before the closing angle bracket. Alternatively, an end tag </img> can be added like this:

```
<img src="url or a file path"></img>
```

Adding a slash before the closing angle bracket is most commonly used. The following example adds an image to the Web page. The image is called `logo.jpg` and it is stored in the same folder as the HTML document on which the image is being inserted.

```
<img src="logo.jpg" />
```

Note that unlike inserting an image in a Microsoft Word document, you are not copying and pasting an image directly into the HTML document. The image is not part of the document itself but remains an external file. This means that when you save an HTML document, the image is *not* saved within the HTML file. The `src` attribute tells the browser where to find the image. Thus, the image file has to exist in the location as specified in the src attribute when the Web browser loads the HTML document. Otherwise, the image will not show up and become what we call a broken image.

3.8 Table

The basic tags for constructing a table are < *table*>, < *tr*>, and < *td*>. Each table definition begins with a <table> tag. A table is divided into rows, designated with the <tr> tag. The letters tr stand for *table row*. The <tr> tags are placed between the <table> and </table> tag.

Each row is divided into data cells using the <td> tag. The letters td stand for *table data*. The <td> tags are placed between the <tr> and </tr> tags. The content intended to appear in a table cell has to be placed between <td> and </td>. If the content is placed within a table element but outside of <td>, how it is displayed in a browser will be unpredictable.

The following example defines a table of two rows and two columns. The text content "This is OK." will be displayed inside the table cells, because they are enclosed within <td> and </td>. However, the text "This line is not OK!!" that is placed outside of <td> will not be displayed inside a table cell.

```
<table>
    This line is not OK!!
    <tr>
        This line is not OK!!
        <td>This is OK.</td>
        This line is not OK!!
        <td>This is OK.</td>
    </tr>
    This line is not OK!!
    <tr>
        <td>This is OK.</td>
        <td>This is OK.</td>
    </tr>
</table>
```

A table cell can contain other HTML elements, such as text, images, lists, forms, and other tables. Note that a table is constructed row by row. Each row is divided into cells. You may think of the cells as columns for each row. Figure 8a shows an example HTML code using these tags to construct a table of three rows and two columns. Figure 8b shows how this table is displayed on a Web browser.

This simple example shows a bare-bones table. Without a table border, it may be hard to tell that it is a table. Figure 9 shows the same table as that in Figure 8, except that a border is added by specifying the border attribute for the <table> tag.

🖱 **HTML: Images and Tables (LAB)** Hand-code three HTML documents:

- One HTML document contains a table with image thumbnails. Clicking on the image thumbnail will go to the page containing the full image.
- Two HTML documents: Each contains the full image of the thumbnail.

```
<!DOCTYPE html PUBLIC "-//W3C//DTD XHTML 1.0 Transitional//EN"
    "http://www.w3.org/TR/xhtml1/DTD/xhtml1-transitional.dtd">
<html xmlns="http://www.w3.org/1999/xhtml">
<head>
<meta http-equiv="Content-Type" content="text/html;
charset=utf-8 /">
<title>Table Example</title>
</head>
<body>
<table>
    <tr>
        <td>row 1, column 1</td>
        <td>row 1, column 2</td>
    </tr>
    <tr>
        <td>row 2, column 1</td>
        <td>row 2, column 2</td>
    </tr>
    <tr>
        <td>row 3, column 1</td>
        <td>row 3, column 2</td>
    </tr>
</table>
</body>
</html>
```

(a)

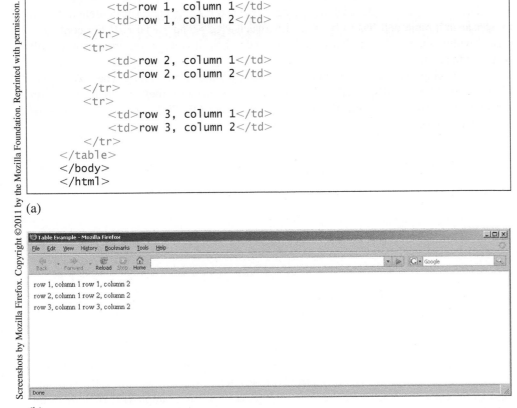

(b)

Figure 8 (a) Full HTML code for a Web page that contains a table without specifying a border, with the tags for constructing the table given in color. (b) How the table looks in a Web browser.

🖰 **Dreamweaver Workspace Overview** An overview of the workspace and most commonly used panels in Adobe Dreamweaver.

🖰 **Web Authoring Using Adobe Dreamweaver (LAB)** Get acquainted with Adobe Dreamweaver. Set up a Web site in Dreamweaver. Create and edit Web pages using the visual editor.

```
<!DOCTYPE html PUBLIC "-//W3C//DTD XHTML 1.0 Transitional//EN"
    "http://www.w3.org/TR/xhtml1/DTD/xhtml1-transitional.dtd">
<html xmlns="http://www.w3.org/1999/xhtml">
<head>
<meta http-equiv="Content-Type" content="text/html;
charset=utf-8 /">
<title>Table Example</title>
</head>
<body>
<table border="1">
    <tr>
        <td>row 1, column 1</td>
        <td>row 1, column 2</td>
    </tr>
    <tr>
        <td>row 2, column 1</td>
        <td>row 2, column 2</td>
    </tr>
    <tr>
        <td>row 3, column 1</td>
        <td>row 3, column 2</td>
    </tr>
</table>
</body>
</html>
```

(a)

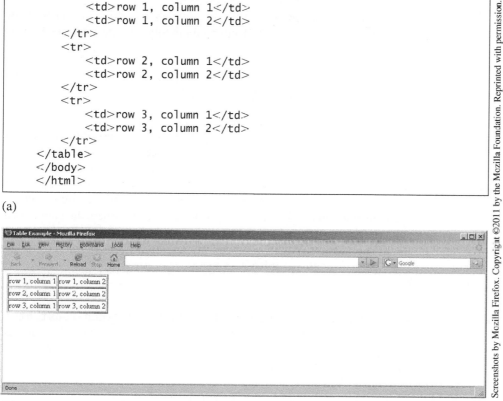

(b)

Figure 9 (a) Full HTML code for a Web page that contains a table with a border.
(b) How the table looks in a Web browser.

4 UNDERSTANDING FILE PATHS

HTML documents, images, sounds, and videos are stored as files on a computer. *Folders* (also called directories) are used to organize files. When you open a folder, you may see other folders and/or files inside the folder. When you open a file, you will see the content of the file. To view the content of a file correctly, you will need to open the file using the right application program—for example, Notepad (Windows) and TextEdit (Mac OS) for plain text files, and Adobe Photoshop for digital images.

4.1 File Paths

A *file path* refers to the location of a file on a computer, like an address to a house. When you address an envelope, you follow a certain order—for example, the name of the person, the street, the city, and then the state or country. Similarly, to write a file path, you write the folder names in the order of the folder hierarchical structure—start from the outermost folder to the inner folders. A file path to a file ends with the filename.

The folder names are separated by a delimiter, which is a forward slash (/) or backslash (\). Forward slashes (/) are used most commonly for file paths in HTML documents.

4.2 Types of File Paths for Web Pages

Suppose someone asks you for directions to see a particular painting in an art exhibition. If the art exhibition is out of town, you probably will give the person a full address, specifying the building, city, and state where the exhibition takes place. On the other hand, if the exhibition is right inside the building you are located at—but on a different floor—then you will give the person directions for how to get to the other floor from where you are standing. The full address with the city and state is also a valid direction, but you would not choose to give such direction in this situation. If you are in the room where the painting is, you may just point to the painting and tell the person that it is right there. You would not even mention the floor and room. You give different types of directions depending on the situation. It is the same for the file paths for Web pages.

There are three types of paths:

- *Absolute Paths.*
  Example: `http://www.mysite.com/products/coffee/french-roast.html`
  This is the full URL to a Web page or any media. It is like giving the full address for an out-of-town art exhibition. If you are linking to a page that is on a different Web site, you will need to use the absolute path.
- *Document-Relative Paths.*
  Example: `products/coffee/french-roast.html`
  This is the most common type of file path in Web authoring. It is like giving directions to get to another floor in the art exhibition scenario or pointing at the painting if you are in the same room of the painting. The direction you give is *relative* to where the person is standing. The direction is only valid for that specific location where the person is. The same direction becomes invalid if the person asks in another building or a different floor of the same building. The example path shown here is relative to where this `french-roast.html` is being requested. You will see examples on constructing document-relative paths in the next subsection.
- *Site Root-Relative Paths.*
  Example: `/products/coffee/french-roast.html`
  A site root-relative path always starts with a forward slash (/). It means starting from the root folder of the site. A *root folder* is the outermost folder of the site structure.

4.3 Rules for Creating Links Using Document-Relative Paths

Suppose you have a site with a folder structures shown in Figure 10. Figure 10 shows two different graphical representations of the folder structure of a site called my-site. The graphical representations help you create a mental model for the relationships of the folders and files in the site.

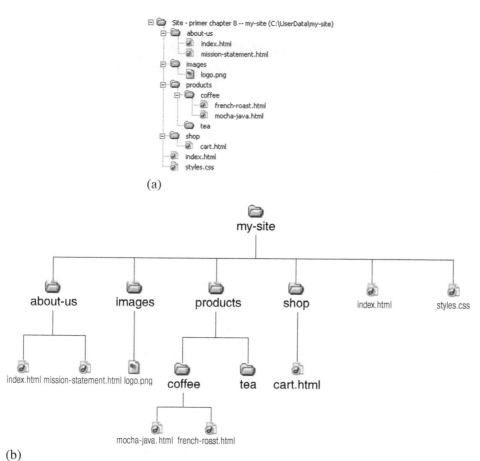

(a)

(b)

Figure 10 Two different visual representations of the folder structure of a site.

In this example, the root folder for the site is called my-site. Inside the my-site folder, there are four folders (about-us, images, products, and shop) and two files (index.html and styles.css). Inside each of these four folders are other folders and files. Figure 11 shows how it looks when you navigate this folder structure on your computer. When you double-click on a folder, you see the folder(s) and file(s) stored there.

To construct a document-relative path, you need to know the relative location between the target page (the page being linked *to*) and the source page (the page containing the link or the page being linked *from*) in the site structure.

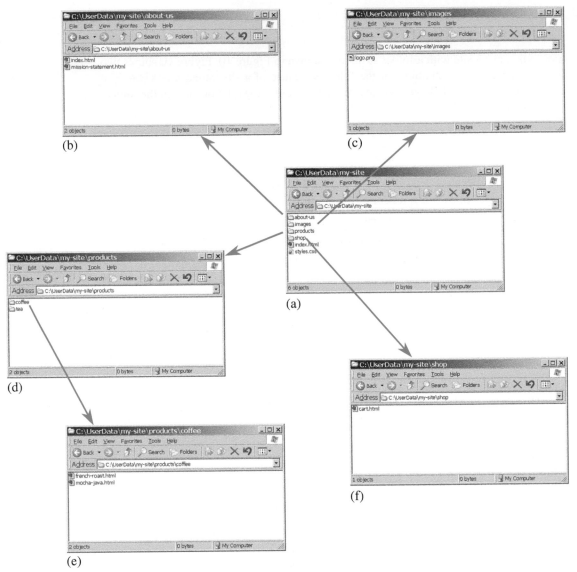

Figure 11 Using windows to navigate the folder structure. (a) A window showing the content of a folder. (b) Opening the folder about-us in (a). (c) Opening the folder images in (a). (d) Opening the folder products in (a). (e) Opening the folder coffee in (d). (f) Opening the folder shop in (a).

Rule #1

To link to another file that is in the same folder as the current document, simply use the filename as the path. For example, to add a link in mocha-java.html to link to french-roast.html (Figure 12), the file path is simply the filename french-roast.html.

Returning to the art exhibition scenario, this is like when the person asking for directions is in the same room as where the painting is. You can simply point to the painting. You do not need any extra information regarding navigation to another building, floor, or room.

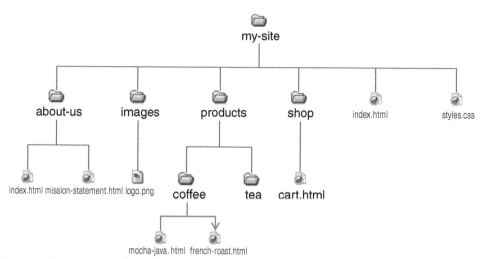

Figure 12 Navigating from `mocha-java.html` to `french-roast.html`.

Rule #2

To link to a file that is in a subfolder of the current document's folder, use the subfolder name followed by a forward slash (/) and then the filename. Each forward slash (/) represents moving down one level in the folder.

For example, to add a link in `index.html` (in `my-site` folder) to link to `french-roast.html` (Figure 13), the relative path is `products/coffee/french-roast.html`.

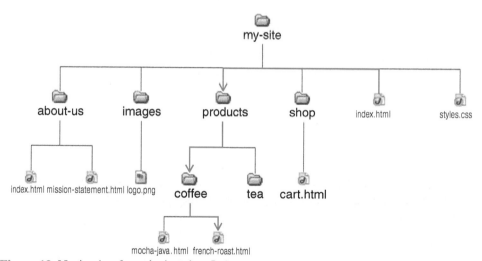

Figure 13 Navigating from `index.html` (in `my-site` folder) to `french-roast.html`.

Rule #3

To link to a file that is outside of the current document's folder, start the path with `../` (where `../` means going up one level in the folder hierarchy), followed by the folder name, a forward slash (/), and then the filename. Multiple `../` can be appended for going up multiple levels in the folder hierarchy.

For example, to add a link in `french-roast.html` to link to `index.html` (in `my-site` folder) (Figure 14), the relative path is `../../index.html`.

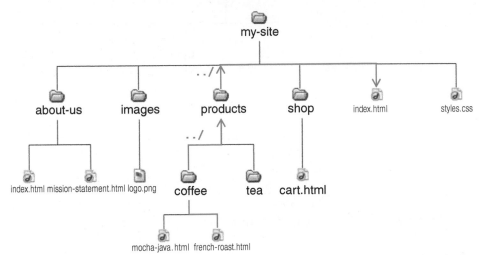

Figure 14 Navigating from `french-roast.html` to `index.html` (in `my-site` folder). `../` is used to indicate going up one level in the folder hierarchy.

To construct the file path that links from `french-roast.html` to `cart.html` (in the `shop` folder) (Figure 15), imagine you have the `coffee` folder open. You see the `french-roast.html` file. From there, to see `cart.html`, you need to follow the following steps.

Step 1 Go up one level (`../`) to get out of the `coffee` folder into the `products` folder.

Step 2 Go up another level (`../`) to get out of the `products` folder into the `my-site` folder.

Step 3 Go into the `shop` folder (`shop/`). Now, you see the `cart.html`. Thus, the relative path is `../../shop/cart.html`.

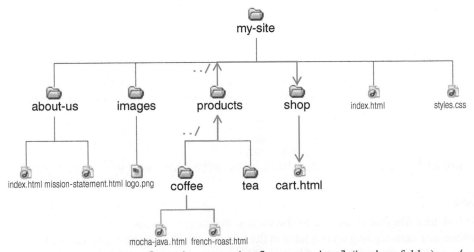

Figure 15 Navigating from `french-roast.html` to `cart.html` (in `shop` folder). `../` used to indicate going up one level in the folder hierarchy.

4.4 Why Is It Important to Understand File Paths for Web Page Creation?

It is essential to understand the file paths in order to create valid links and embed images. File paths are used in the HTML document for the hyperlinked files, such as HTML documents, images, and videos. A path serves as a direction or address to retrieve the linked files. Incorrect paths lead to broken images or broken links on Web pages.

Web page editing programs let you insert images and links using a graphical interface, and they automatically construct relative paths for you. You seldom need to figure out file paths. If you rename or move files and folders around in your site, those file paths inserted in your HTML document prior to the change will no longer be valid and will need to be updated. Web site management programs (such as Adobe Dreamweaver) can automatically update the file paths for renamed and moved files if you rename or move the files within the program. However, if you do not use the program to rename or move the files of your site, the links will not be updated automatically. You may use the program to check for broken links and fix them. Nevertheless, being able to read and construct the file paths helps troubleshoot broken links without having to rely on a program; in some situations, you do not have access to such a program.

5 SUMMARY

The term *Web pages* refers to documents that are written in a language called HTML. HTML stands for Hypertext Markup Language. An HTML file is a text file. The text formatting, tabs, and line breaks in the text file do not appear when the document is viewed on a Web browser. However, the text can be marked with markup tags that tell the Web browser how to display the page. A Web browser is an application that can display the HTML document in the correct format and layout according to the markup tags. An HTML document can be created using a text editor, such as Notepad in Windows or TextEdit in Mac OS. It also can be created using a Web page editor, such as Adobe Dreamweaver.

XHTML stands for Extensible Hypertext Markup Language. It is intended to be a replacement for HTML. It is almost identical to the HTML 4.01 standard but has stricter rules for writing HTML.

Style sheets allow you to define styles to display HTML elements. Multiple style definitions can be combined or cascaded into one—thus the term *cascading style sheets*.

JavaScript is a scripting language for Web pages. It can be used to generate the Web page content in response to the user's interaction. Dynamic HTML (DHTML) is a combination of HTML, CSS, and JavaScript. When combined with CSS, JavaScript can be used to control properties such as text styles, color, visibility, and positioning of HTML elements dynamically.

URL stands for Uniform Resource Locator. This is the standard for specifying the address of Web pages and other resources on the World Wide Web.

Markup tags come in pairs, for example, <p> and </p>. The first tag, <p>, is the start tag. The second tag, </p>, is the end tag or closing tag. Tags may have attributes. Attributes of a tag specify the properties of the element.

Introduction to HTML

The very basic, bare-bones structure of an HTML document looks like this:

```
<html>
<head>
<title>This is a title.</title>
</head>
<body>
This is the content of the Web page.
</body>
</html>
```

An XHTML document has the same basic structure as an HTML document, plus it has a DOCTYPE declaration.

Common tags are introduced in the chapter. These include: `<p>`, `<br>`, `<h1>`–`<h6>`, `<b>`, `<i>`, `<strong>`, `<em>`, `<a>`, `<img>`, and tags for tables.

A file path refers to the location of a file on a computer. There are three types of paths used in an HTML document:

- Absolute Paths: This is the full URL to a Web page or any media, for example: `http://www.mysite.com/products/coffee/french-roast.html`.
- Document-Relative Paths: The path is relative to where a file is being requested, for example, `products/coffee/french-roast.html`.
- Site Root-Relative Paths: A site root-relative path always starts with a forward slash (/), for example: `/products/coffee/french-roast.html`. A path starting with a forward slash means starting from the root folder of the site. A root folder is the outermost folder of the site structure.

TERMS

`<a>`	folders	`<p>`
absolute path	`<h1>`	root folder
anchor tag	`<h2>`	site root-relative paths
attributes	`<h3>`	start tag
`<b>`	`<h4>`	`<strong>`
` `	`<h5>`	style sheets
cascading style sheets	`<h6>`	`<table>`
(CSS)	HTML	tags
closing tag	http	`<td>`
DOCTYPE	Hypertext Markup	`<tr>`
document-relative path	Language	`<ul>`
dynamic HTML	Hypertext Transfer	Uniform Resource
(DHTML)	Protocol	Locator
`<em>`	`<i>`	unordered list
element content	`<img>`	URL
end tag	JavaScript	Web browser
Extensible Hypertext	`<li>`	Web pages
Markup Language	`<ol>`	Web site
file path	ordered list	XHTML

LEARNING AIDS

The following learning aids can be found at the text's companion Web site.

🖰 **HTML: Basic HTML Document Structure, Paragraphs, Line Breaks, Lists, Links, Heading, Bold and Italics Text (Lab)**
Hand code two HTML documents using basic HTML document structure.

🖰 **HTML: Images and Tables (Lab)**
Hand-code three HTML documents:

- One HTML document contains a table with image thumbnails. Clicking on the image thumbnail will go to the page containing the full image.
- Two HTML documents: Each contains the full image of the thumbnail.

🖰 **Dreamweaver Workspace Overview**
An overview of the workspace and most commonly used panels in Adobe Dreamweaver.

🖰 **Web Authoring Using Adobe Dreamweaver (Lab)**
Get acquainted with Adobe Dreamweaver. Set up a Web site in Dreamweaver. Create and edit Web pages using the visual editor.

REVIEW QUESTIONS

When applicable, please select all correct answers.

1. HTML documents are _____.

   A. text files
   B. JPG files
   C. PSD files
   D. MP3 files

2. Dynamic HTML is a combination of _____, _____, and _____.

3. **True/False:** Dynamic HTML is a special programming language by itself.

4. For the URL: `http://www.schoolname.edu/departments/art/index.html`:

   i. The domain name of the Web server is _____.
   ii. This URL is a Web address of a file named _____.
   iii. This file is located in the folder named _____, which is inside another folder named _____.

5. _____ are markup codes in an HTML document that tell the Web browser how to format the text when displaying it.

   A. Attributes   B. Tags

6. In the HTML code:
   `<p>This is a paragraph.</p>`
   `<p>` is the _____, and `</p>` is the _____. The text "`This is a paragraph.`" is the _____.

   A. element content; start tag; end tag   B. element content; end tag; start tag
   C. start tag; end tag; element content   D. start tag; element content; end tag
   E. end tag; start tag; element content   F. end tag; element content; start tag

7. Fill in the correct start tags and end tags to create a basic HTML document.

```
<_____>
<_____>
<_____>This is the page title.<_____>
<_____>
<_____>
This is the content of the Web page.
<_____>
<_____>
```

8. Describe briefly how XHTML is different from HTML in terms of each of the following:
   i. Tag pairing
   ii. Cases of tags
   iii. Tag nesting
   iv. Root element of a page
   v. DOCTYPE declaration

9. The _____ tag is used to create a line break—to force a new line without starting a new paragraph. By default, the line created using this tag has _____-line spacing.

10. The _____ tag is used to create a heading 1 element.

11. Fill in the blanks for the HTML code below to create a link to your favorite Web site. Use a valid URL.

```
<_____ _____ = "_____">My Favorite Web site<_____>
```

12. Fill in the blanks for the HTML code below to embed an image called logo.jpg on a Web page. Suppose logo.jpg is in the same folder as the HTML document that embeds it.

```
<_____ _____ = "_____" _____>
```

13. Fill in the blanks for the HTML code to create a list as shown.

   1. Preheat oven to 450 degrees.
   2. Heat butter and oil in a large saucepan.
   3. Cook the shrimp for 10 minutes.

```
<_____>
<_____>Preheat oven to 450 degrees.<_____>
<_____>Heat butter and oil in a large saucepan.<_____>
<_____>Cook the shrimp for 10 minutes.<_____>
<_____>
```

14. Fill in the blanks for the HTML code to create a list as shown.

   • Elephants
   • Tigers
   • Frogs

```
<_____>
<_____>Elephants<_____>
<_____>Tigers<_____>
<_____>Frogs<_____>
<_____>
```

15. Fill in the blanks for the HTML code to create a table as shown.

Elephants	Tulips
Tigers	Roses

```
<table>
    <tr>
        <td>_____</td>
        <td>_____</td>
    <_____>
    <tr>
        <td>_____</td>
        <td>_____</td>
    <_____>
<_____>
```

16. For the site shown in Figure 10, to add a link on the page mocha-java.html to link to the Web page french-roast.html, the document-relative file path is _____.

17. For the site shown in Figure 10, to embed the image logo.png on the homepage index.html (in the my-site folder), the document-relative file path is _____.

18. For the site shown in Figure 10, to embed the image logo.png on the Web page french-roast.html, the document-relative file path is _____.

(a) A natural image. (b) Imagine a grid of 25 × 20 cells is applied on the image. (c) The color of each of the 25 × 20 grid cells is averaged to a single value. (d) Imagine a grid of 100 × 80 cells is applied on the image. (e) The color of each of the 100 × 80 grid cells is averaged to a single value.

(a)   (b)

The relative sizes of an image
25 pixels × 20 pixels (left) and
100 pixels × 80 pixels (right) captured
from the same scene.

(a)   (b)

(a) A 4-color palette. (b) An
8-color palette.

(a)   (b)

The sampled image is quantized into (a) four colors, and (b) eight colors.

(a)   (b)

(a) The colors in the original image (b) are quantized into four colors using the palette
shown in Figure 2.3a. Some of the similar green colors, such as those in the outlined square
box, are now mapped to a single color.

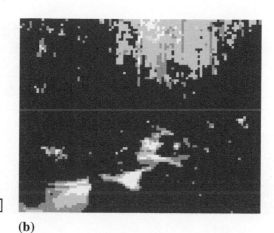

(a)	**(b)**

(a) Using a different 8-color palette, (b) the sampled image is quantized.

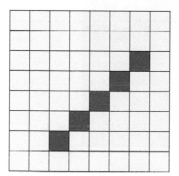

1	1	1	1	1	1	1	1
1	1	1	1	1	1	1	1
1	1	1	1	1	1	0	1
1	1	1	1	1	0	1	1
1	1	1	1	0	1	1	1
1	1	1	0	1	1	1	1
1	1	0	1	1	1	1	1
1	1	1	1	1	1	1	1

For each pixel in a 1-bit (i.e., 2-color) bitmap image, its color value can be represented by 0s and 1s.

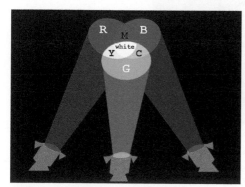

RGB: An additive color system.

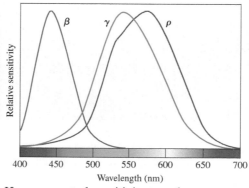

Human spectral sensitivity to color.

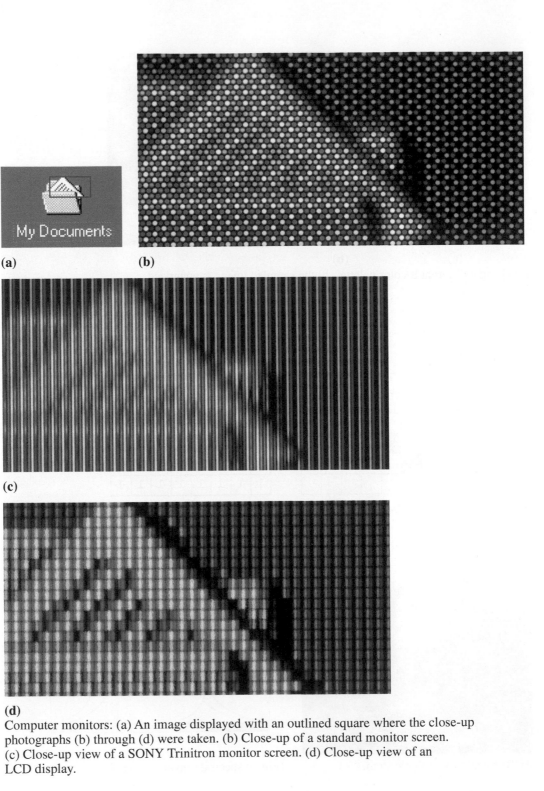

(a)

(b)

(c)

(d)
Computer monitors: (a) An image displayed with an outlined square where the close-up photographs (b) through (d) were taken. (b) Close-up of a standard monitor screen. (c) Close-up view of a SONY Trinitron monitor screen. (d) Close-up view of an LCD display.

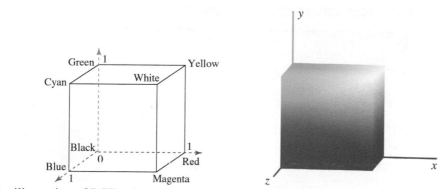

An illustration of RGB color cube.

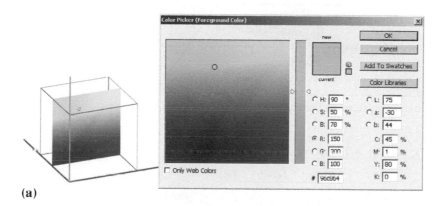

(a)

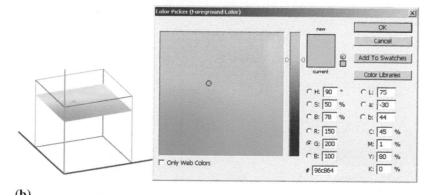

(b)

Relationship between an RGB color cube and the color picker used in digital image applications. (*continued*)

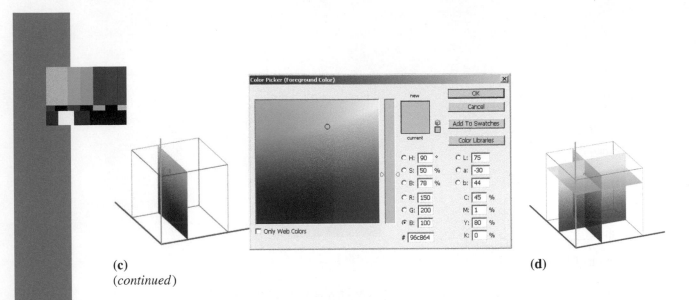

(c)
(continued)

(d)

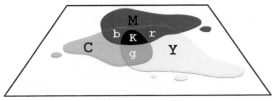

CMYK: A subtractive color system. In theory, mixing cyan, magenta, and yellow gives black.

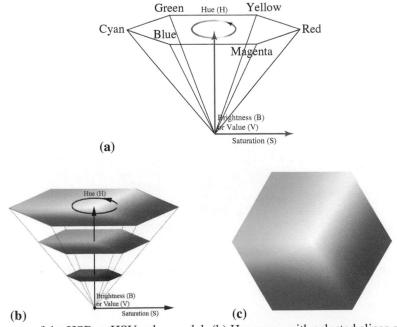

(a)

(b)

(c)

(a) Hexacone of the HSB or HSV color model. (b) Hexacone with selected slices at different levels of brightness or value. (c) A slice of the color wheel from the HSB or HSV color model.

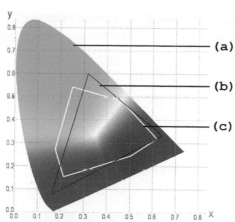

An illustration for color gamut comparison: (a) A CIE chromaticity diagram. (b) RGB color gamut of typical CRT monitors. The exact shape of the device's color space depends on the monitor's red, green, and blue phosphors. Note that this does not include all the colors humans can see. (c) CMYK color gamut of typical inkjet printers. The exact shape of the color space depends on the colorants of the printer's ink.

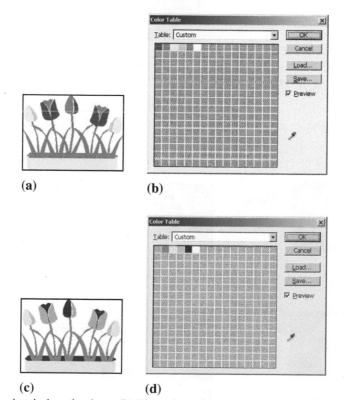

(a) An image using indexed colors. (b) The color table or palette for the indexed colors. (c) The image with changes made to the indexed colors. (d) The color table that is used by the image in (c).

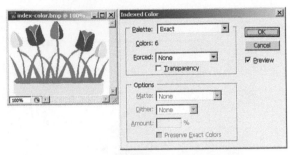

An image is converted to indexed-color mode.

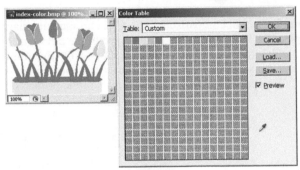

The first color (index 0) on the color table is changed to a light blue.

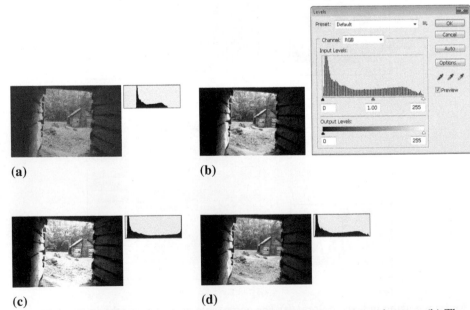

(a)

(b)

(c)

(d)

Scanned images with their histograms: (a) Scanned using a narrow tonal range. (b) The tonal range of the scanned image (a) is adjusted by stretching the histogram. (c) Scanned with highlights cropped off. (d) Scanned with a maximized tonal range.

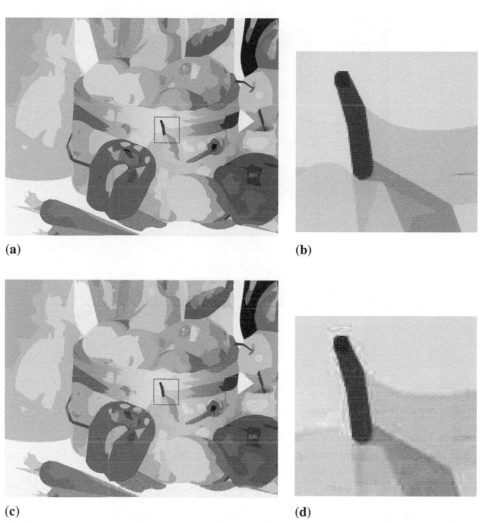

(a) An uncompressed image. (b) A zoom-in view of the area outlined in the colored box in image (a). (c) A highly compressed JPEG image of (a). (d) A zoom-in view of the area outlined in color in the JPEG image (b) showing the JPEG artifact.

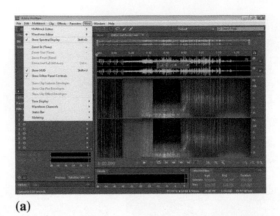

(a)

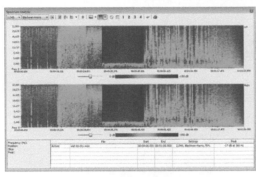

(b)

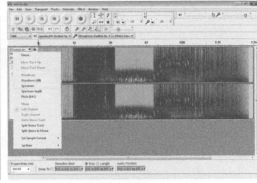

(c)

Spectral view of audio in Figure 5.10. (a) Adobe Audition CS5.5: `View > Show Spectral Display`. (b) Sony Sound Forge 10: `View > Spectrum Analysis` and click the Sonogram button. (c) Audacity 1.3 Beta: `Spectrum`.

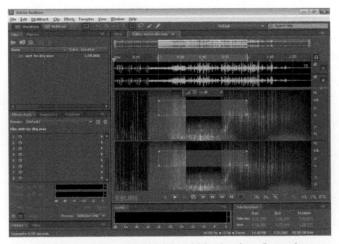

The frequency range of about 4,000 to 10,000 Hz within the time frame between 20 second and 1 minute is selected (as indicated by the pale rectangle) in the spectral view.

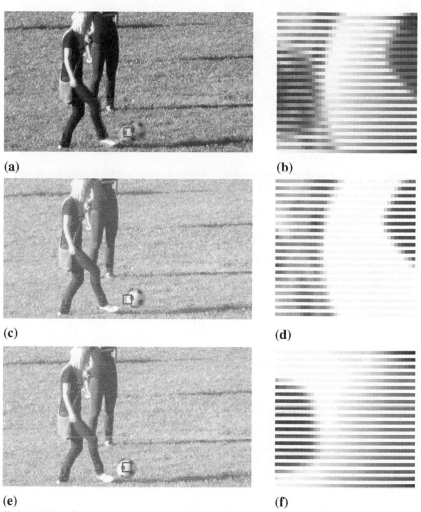

(a) A digital video frame showing comb-like artifact caused by fast action and camera panning. (b) Close-up of the small outlined area in (a). (c) The upper field of the video frame. (d) Close-up of the small outlined area in (c). (e) The lower field of the video frame. (f) Close-up of the small outlined area in (e).

(a) The video frame deinterlaced by eliminating the upper field and interpolating the lower field to fill in the gaps. (b) Close-up of the small outlined area.

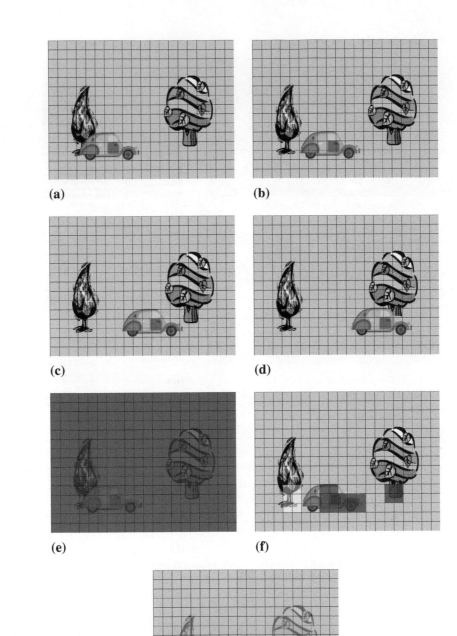

(a) through (d) The first four frames of a video: (a) Frame 1, being the reference frame or the I-frame. (b) Frame 2, being a B-frame. (c) Frame 3, being a B-frame. (d) Frame 4, being a P-frame. (e) through (g) Areas highlighted in red are original pixel information and areas highlighted in blue are from the previous I-frame. Areas highlighted in cyan are from the previous I-frame at the same location, and those highlighted in yellow are from the next P-frame.

Note: Not all the blocks are labeled for their encoding method; only some are highlighted to illustrate the points.

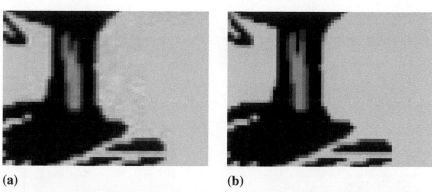

(a)   **(b)**

(a) MPEG artifact, discernible at the intersect area of dark and light colors. (b) The original image before MPEG compression.

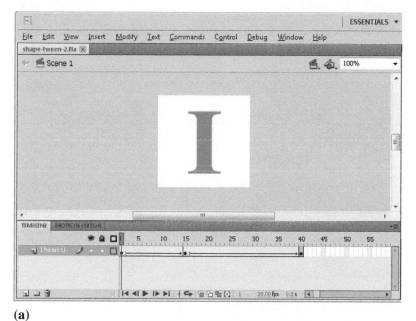

(a)

A shape tweened animation. (a) Keyframe at frame 1. (*continued*)

(b)

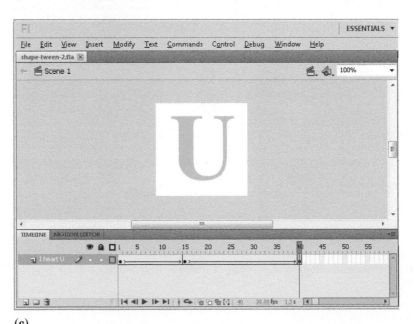

(c)

(*continued*) (b) In the second keyframe (frame 15), the shape and color are altered. (c) In the last keyframe of this animation sequence (frame 40), the shape and color are further altered.

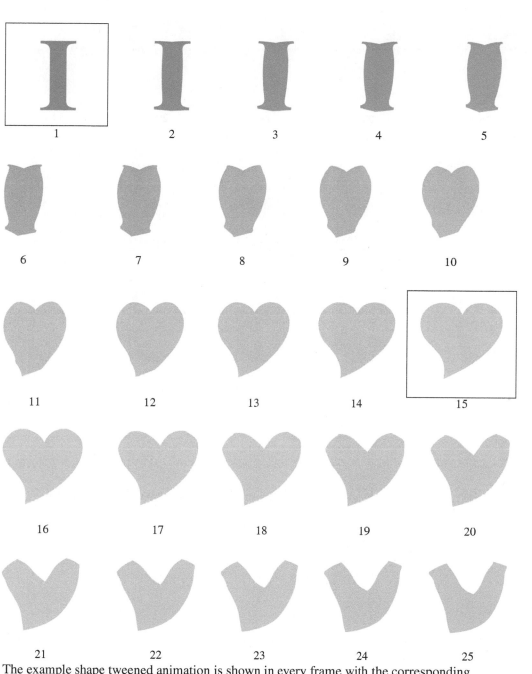

The example shape tweened animation is shown in every frame with the corresponding frame number, where frames 1, 15, and 40 are the keyframes where the shapes are explicitly specified. (*continued*)

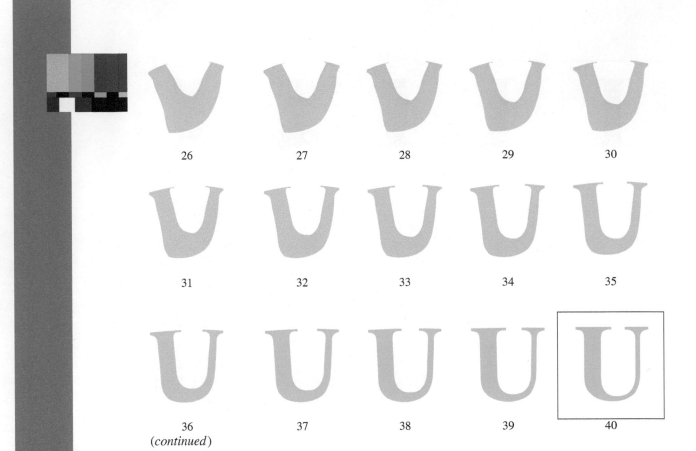

26   27   28   29   30

31   32   33   34   35

36   37   38   39   40

(*continued*)

Index

217